My Body Would be the Kindest of Strangers

My Body Would be the Kindest of Strangers

Fiona Helmsley

Many of the stories and essays in this book have been published online, or in anthologies, often in slightly different versions:

"A Rite of Passage for a Boy Who Grew Up in a Trunk" and "Final Notice" at *Junk Lit*; "Arm Candy" at *PANK* and in the book *How Dirty Girls Get Clean*; "Souvenirs" at *Vol. 1 Brooklyn*; "Killing Michael J. Fox," "Herbert Huncke Herbert Huncke Herbert Huncke," and "Joan Vollmer Burroughs Died for Somebody's Sins not Mine" at *Paragraph Line*; "The Optimism of Being a Dope Fiend" at *The Rumpus* and in the book *Ladyland*; "Captain Save-A-Ho" at *The Rumpus* and in the books *Johns, Marks, Tricks and Chickenhawks: Professionals and Their Clients Writing about Each Other* and *The Best Sex Writing of the Year*; "A Totally Gruesome Document Detailing a Relationship" at *The Weeklings*; "They All Want to Piss on You" at *Horror, Sleaze, Trash*; "Kill Your Idols" in the book *Do You Love Me?: The Gene Gregorits File*; "Thoughts on the Shit Show" at *HTMLGIANT* and in the zine *The Oakland Review*; "Aisles of Opportunity" at *Entropy*; "The Satanic How-to Guide to Exalted Girldom" at *The Hairpin*; "Pray to St. Anthony" at *The Fanzine*; "Live Through This: Twenty Years in Love with Courtney Love" at *The Fix*; and "The Whore Box" at *Human Parts* on *Medium*.

Paragraph Line Books
Oakland, CA
http://www.paragraphline.com

¶|

ISBN: 978-1-942086-02-4
PL-114

For Amber and Jason

I was born doing reference work in sin, and born confessing it. This is what poems are...the rat's star. — *Anne Sexton*

I don't even want to talk about "female sexuality" until there is a control group. And there never will be. — *Maggie Nelson*

Table of Contents

A Rite of Passage for a Boy Who Grew Up in a Trunk

We were each other's first drug-damaged relationship. He was tortured, I was callous. His pet name for me, when we could laugh about it, was *Fiunkie*. We came together at a pivotal time in both our lives.

After high school, his mom wanted him to move out of the trailer she had raised him in. She said space was getting tight, and it was time he flew the coop. The trailer had sloping floors, and holes you could fall through if you didn't know where to step. It reminded me of a trunk with little compartments that I had played with as a young girl in my great-grandmother's attic. It seemed to me that this boy had grown up in a trunk. Early in our relationship, I gave him crabs after having sex with a boy in a coffee shop bathroom and convinced him that he had given them to me from something he picked up inside the trailer.

My mother loved him. She thought he'd be a good influence on me, and agreed to let him move in. Later, she would tell me she never knew he was my boyfriend, and always believed we were just good friends.

She had reason to think he was not my boyfriend.

The world was a very different place from the world I'd known just the year before. In this new world, every boy I wanted to fuck wanted to fuck me. I could not resist these sparkling riches. I had never been the girl who inspired strong physical desire. I had always been her funny friend.

Our relationship quickly devolved into psychodrama.

Which is not to say we did not have our moments of bliss, of borderline, relative normalcy. We travelled across the country, broadcast a public access show, and formed a few one-off, one-night punk rock bands. Two movies I wrote and he directed were on video compilations by Miranda July. We made 'zines and were prolific creative partners. But something hungered inside of me that could only be fed by boys and by drugs.

He didn't do heroin, and I believe, initially, this aspect of my lifestyle intrigued him. It filled in some blanks. His father had been a heroin addict who had died from drug-related illness when he was fifteen. He had never known his father, and his father's parents hid from him when they saw him in the supermarket. All he had of his dad's, besides what he saw when he looked in the mirror, was a small box-style television set that his mother went out of her way to tell him had come from a pawn shop. This small gift lent itself naturally to the creative passion of his life. He was obsessed with film and used the small television set to edit his low-budget movies from 8mm to VHS. He had never lived with his father nor experienced the intricacies of his addiction first-hand, but his father's absence could only permeate every aspect of his life.

By not being there, you are. Sometimes even more so.

Your first druggy relationship is a rite of passage. A learning experience with a curve. After that one, the next one, if there is a next one, will be a decision. You will know just what you are getting into.

At first, it was about catching me in lies. If he could just get me to admit to them, get me to acknowledge that I was found out, then I would have to stop. The shame of being caught could only stop me dead in my tracks. When I wouldn't give up anything, he started following me. I could no longer deny, deny, deny when he had seen with his own eyes. One luminous spring afternoon, I was riding shotgun in a friend's car on our way to go cop heroin in East Haven, when I looked over to the next lane of traffic and saw him in the car next to ours, waving. He had followed us for over thirty minutes just for that moment. When trailing me made no difference, he began confronting my friends, an incredibly awkward endeavor, as many of my friends were also his own, and they respected him, as this crazy, backwoods genius, the only one of us still doing anything worthwhile as we all dissolved into liars and thieves. But in addiction, none of that matters. Respect just gets in the way. It's much easier to reach your goals if you can push it aside. So they lied to his face, and he knew that they were lying, and he became bitter, and isolated. In desperation, he went to my family, but they were distracted and living their lives. My mother had just gotten remarried and deserved to have her first real happiness in years free of the black cloud of my issues. Wasn't that the real reason she had allowed him to move in anyway, so that he would help to protect me from myself? Finally, he would leave, but he really had nowhere else to go, and wherever that was, he took his love for me with him, and always came back. I would measure the seriousness of his threat to go by what he had done with his bags. Had he actually packed them? Was he taking them out to the car? If so, had he taken out his guitar yet, because I knew he'd been stashing twenty-dollar bills behind its broken bridge plate...

One afternoon, I came home from work to change my clothes. My friend Phillip would be arriving any minute to pick me up so we could go and cop.

Unexpectedly, he came home.

"Where are you going?" he asked, knowing full well.

"Out for a little while," I answered, trying to keep it light.

Suddenly, something occurred to him and he ran back to our bedroom. I could hear him moving things around on the other side of the door. He sprang back down the hallway, holding his guitar by its neck, the broken bridge plate hanging loose by its two remaining screws.

"You bitch," he said. "Give me back the money that you took."

He lunged for my bag on the table, but I grabbed it first, grasping it tightly to my chest. He clung to its dangling shoulder strap as a means to yank it from my hands. In the commotion, he caught his leg on the side of a chair and fell to the floor, taking me and the bag down with him.

We had never fought like this before, rolling around, me trying desperately to protect what was his. I just needed to get away from him, to free myself and the bag with his money still inside. Over the acoustics of our scuffle, I could make out the sound of a car coming up the driveway. I was so close, if I could just free myself from the weight of his body holding me there on the floor.

I was able to wiggle free for a moment, but he grabbed me by my legs and pulled me back. We rolled into the living room, close to a hutch my mother had decorated with a silver serving tray and two pewter candlesticks. I heard a car door open in the driveway and reached up, grabbed one of the candlesticks and whacked him in the face.

The world stopped and I closed my eyes. I moved my hand across the floor and felt the bag there, free. I would open my eyes again once I got outside.

Then I heard his voice.

"You fucking bitch!"

And I opened them, to be prepared for whatever happened next.

Blood poured from above his lip. It covered his teeth like a coating of cherry dip on a Dairy Queen sundae.

Outside the house, someone was knocking on the door.

He looked at me, the hurt, the anger, the betrayal so fierce and alive in his bloodied face, and spit his blood all over me.

Then he got up from the floor and went into the bathroom.

Unbelievably, it was not Phillip at the door but our friend Travis. Travis probably wanted to cop too, but we hadn't made any plans.

"What the fuck happened?" Travis asked incredulously, surveying the room: the upended furniture, the blood on the floor, on my face and shirt. The strap from my bag lay loose on the carpet, ripped free from its stitching.

Before I could answer, I again heard the sounds of a car coming up the driveway, this time followed by the familiar honk of a horn.

"Travis," I said, "You'll do this for me, won't you? You'll take him to the hospital?"

I did not wait for his response. I went to throw my bag over my shoulder, but it no longer had a strap. So I tucked it under my arm, and went out the door.

Arm Candy

"I want to tell you something, Fi-fi," she says, leaning in and over, her cinnamon breath on my face, and the peaks of her new breasts visible under my Miley Cyrus tank top which will never be the same. It's a tiny bathroom.

She pauses to yank up the top of her pants as they slip down the tops of her thighs. Her business is done, but her belt isn't, and anyway, she desperately wants me to see. She stands up to throw the toilet paper into the wastebasket, hoping to garner a few extra hopeful moments of revelation, but it matters for naught, as I won't look.

"Once I gave up on love, Fi-fi, I gained a new freedom. Nobody can ever hurt me again. And I no longer have to live up to anyone else's standards. I've also never paid for a drink a day since then."

I think how this will no longer be much of a consolation if she goes back to AA tomorrow like she's been planning.

"I want to share them with the world!" she says, fondling her new mountainous flesh formations. I think of Mary Tyler Moore turning the world on with her smile, but I suspect she would have no idea who that is.

"Eventually they will require maintenance," she whines. "No one ever talks about that aspect of augmentation." Her pants are up now, her belt is fastened.

"Let's let some douchebags tell us how pretty we are," she declares. I hold the door.

She knows I've written about her before, and sometimes I feel like she's putting on a show in hopes that I will do it again. Men can give her only five minutes of pleasure while I offer an eternity.

Our relationship is complex. We're more like sisters, and then she reads my mind: "I'd really like to sit here with my sister, mister," she says to the man sitting next to the only open barstool. "Move now, and you can sniff our seats later."

Her crudeness is a punch and a hug. She is a punch and a hug. Everything is offset by her good looks, a genetic blessing with a timestamp and a gender clause. She knows not to push it with women unless they've been prescreened.

The man moves.

Like a date, I'm often proud to have her on my arm.

But sometimes I want to clamp my hand over her mouth knowing that she would squirm and bite. It would be the ultimate indignity in her mind, next to being 86'd by a fat, ugly bouncer.

There are nights when we are together where I've never felt closer to another human being.

Later, she fucks a man from the bar in the bed I'm trying to sleep in, scream-moaning in mock ecstasy to ensure I will awaken in case I've finally fallen asleep. I concede defeat, and get up and move out to the couch.

If I try to look away she will always find a way to make me see.

I am not entirely innocent. The next morning, we both take an extra-long time before we get into the shower, circling each other naked, but only I keep eye contact the entire time.

Aisles of Opportunity

It's strange coming back to the town you grew up in. You see people you would rather not. Transitory people. People who were in your life for just a moment, then, thankfully, they were gone, though what you experienced with them still registered powerfully in your psyche. You see who these people mated with. What their DNA looks like combined with the DNA of another person. You wonder what that other person might think if they knew about your experience.

One of the people I keep seeing around town, wife and small child in tow, is Keith Squires. Keith Squires was a year ahead of me in high school. My older sister got to know him first, and told him all about me—that I was into punk rock, just like him; that he and I shared other interests, like skateboarding; that we both ordered things through the mail from Burning Airlines. She sort of hyped me up a bit, and my freshman year of high school, Keith and I were in the same art class. I guess because of what my sister had said, he assumed that he and I would fall into some kind of numinous relationship. And maybe we would have, had he not been such a liar.

My sister hadn't known he was a liar because she didn't know the little details, like how Gorilla Biscuits had broken up, making it impossible for Keith to always go see them play live in New York, as he claimed, and she didn't know anything about skateboarding, so she believed him when he said he was being vetted by Vision for his skateboarding, and Burton for his snowboarding. But I knew the little details, and it was apparent to me that Keith Squires was full of shit. In art class, he and I sat at the same table, where he would regale me all period long with stories of impossible shows and phony feats and I would sit there and nod along, *uh-huh, uh-huh, uh-huh.* I wasn't interested in calling him out or humiliating him. Besides the lies (for me, a deal-breaking "besides"), he seemed alright. He could be funny, and was good-looking, though he had a greasy bulb of a nose. *If only he'd deep-clean with Noxzema and tell the truth,* I'd say to my friend Meggie, who was also in our art class. *He could be cool.*

One day during art, Keith took Meggie aside and told her he planned on asking me to the school dance. Meggie, of course, told me right away, and we immediately went about planning how I could avoid Keith Squires for the rest of the week. It seemed easier to just avoid him rather than deal with the discomfort and potential for hurt feelings that might come from just saying *no.*

At the end of the day, Keith showed up at my locker. I had two friends with me in anticipation of this, and they swarmed around me like bodyguards.

"I need to talk to you," he said.

"Oops! Gotta go!" I answered, dashing off. "Talk to me in art on Monday!"

Monday, being *after* the dance.

I would have preferred to have given Keith some kind of excuse, like I was going to be out of town, or had other plans for that night, but my friends and I were planning on *going* to the dance. We didn't normally attend school functions, but we'd gotten some acid, and planned on taking it, and dressing up. I was looking forward to going to the dance, just not as the date of Keith Squires.

That night, Keith looked handsome enough in a linen Jimmy Z's suit, but tripping on acid made the oil on his nose appear amplified. That area of his face looked illuminated and slippery, as if it had been lacquered with the insides of one of those oil-slick stickers that you can move around with your fingers. Vulnerable to the profundity of thought that LSD use can inspire, it occurred to me that the oil on Keith's nose might be a mark of his mendacity, like the way Pinocchio's grew whenever he told a lie in the fairy tale. The dance was held inside the high school's cafeteria, and as had now become my practice, I steered clear of Keith Squires.

My friend Amanda had a fight with her boyfriend, and because she was tripping, started to act erratically. She'd stuffed her bra with tissues from the refreshment table and kept pulling them out from her cleavage to wipe the tears from her eyes. The dance chaperones were getting suspicious of her behavior, so we decided to leave. As I was going out the door, someone grabbed my arm.

"You could have just said *no*," Keith Squires said.

I wasn't sure if it was just the effects of the LSD, but his words sounded ominous. That his nose seemed to be alive and pulsating didn't help.

The next week, Keith moved to a different table in art class. When we ran into each other during class or in the hallways, he would laugh to himself, or mutter indecipherably. It was clear he held some sort of resentment against me, but because he was a year ahead of me, we had no other classes together for almost three years.

By the end of his senior year and my junior one, Keith Squires had blossomed into quite a good looking fellow. So good looking, that, although he had few male friends because of his continued affinity for tall tales, he'd acquired quite a few female ones. His nose was less greasy, and he had grown dreadlocks, a good look for him. But while things had gotten better for Keith on the girl-front, they weren't so good on the academic-front; he was moved into my junior year English class. The muttering around me had stopped, but we hadn't spoken since my freshman year. During class, he would make jokes out loud, trying too hard to be funny. Sometimes our classmates laughed, but most of the time his attempts at humor were met with an awkward silence. We already had a class clown, one from our own grade. No one really knew what to make of Keith Squires.

One day, the teacher broke the class up into small groups to work on an assignment. Keith and I were put into the same group, in what was our closest physical proximity to each other in years. The teacher gave out heavy-duty, hardcover Webster's dictionaries for each group to use. The dictionaries were piled high on a table near her desk, and she handed them out to each group one at a time, because they were so big. She put our group's dictionary on Keith's desk, then left the room for a moment to make more photocopies. As our group began to go over the assignment, I bent down to pick up my notebook from the floor, and something heavy and hard slammed into the back of my head.

The two other members of our group, quiet, mousey kids who I had no real rapport with, clearly had no idea how to respond. I had a reputation for being a loud, brash girl, so maybe they thought I could handle what had happened all by myself. My eyes flooded with tears, from the violence of the act, from the profound shock of it. Keith Squires had hit me in the back of my skull with our group's dictionary. After ricocheting off the back of my head, the book fell to the floor with a thud and the rest of the class looked over in our direction. Keith Squires did not look up from his desk; he kept his eyes focused on the paperwork in front of him, but the upturned corners of his mouth were visible. Keith Squires was smiling.

Staring at the dictionary on the ground, there was one thought in my mind, one very powerful and oppressive thought, and it was that I would not let Keith Squires see me cry. Since I refused to give him the satisfaction, I couldn't move. I couldn't speak. Because if I did, I would not just cry. I would quake. Keith Squires could have fractured my skull. It was just dumb luck that he hadn't.

There was silence at our table, except for the two mousey kids, nervously trying to discuss the assignment. A few minutes later, the teacher returned to the room.

I never said a thing.

***

Three times in the last two months, I have seen Keith Squires and his wife and small child in the supermarket. The last time, I found myself all alone with his wife in the cereal aisle as Keith and his small child shopped somewhere else in the store. I fantasized about approaching her, asking her to pass me a box of Frosted Flakes, then introducing myself and explaining my tenuous, violent connection to her husband.

Could you pass me that box of cereal, and did you know that nineteen years ago, your husband brained me with a dictionary during English class because I didn't want to go to a school dance with him, almost three years before that?

I think she would probably look at me blankly, the same way my classmates and I used to look at Keith whenever he tried to be funny during English.

Then, while I still had her attention, I'd continue:

You know why I think he did it, Mrs. Squires? I think that as a result of the rejection he felt, I became less than human to him. Like he righted the slight in his mind by viewing me as a lesser life-form, like a bug or something. I think every breath I took after that was like a buzzing in his ear— but it was tolerable buzzing, because we were never around each other. We didn't have any classes together, so he didn't have to see me, or hear me buzz. Then, when we were put together in the same group during English, my buzzing was back, so he tried to squash me once and for all with that dictionary.

At this point, I'm sure Mrs. Squires would be wheeling her cart, trying to get away from me. She would have decided I was some crazy person, even if there were parts of my story she could relate to. I'd probably have to trail after her, my voice getting louder:

You know what I think about sometimes, Mrs. Squires? I think about the three years your husband waited and the implement that he used in terms of escalating presents for wedding anniversaries. You know, on a one-year anniversary, the gift is paper, on a second-year anniversary, the gift is cotton, on a third -year anniversary...the gift is a dictionary to the back of the head.

And in those same terms, I think about what my implement might look like, nineteen years later. It was opportunism that led your husband to use that dictionary during English class. And here in the supermarket, Mrs. Squires, I have aisles and aisles of opportunity.

Souvenirs

The first time I ever saw a dead body was on a subway platform. It was the body of a white man, dressed business casual, in khaki pants, and black dress shoes. I couldn't see his face or the upper part of his body, it had been covered with plastic. He was slumped backwards on a bench, his body held up by the wall behind it. He was freshly dead, *The New York Times* he'd been reading at his feet, sections on *Business*, and ironically, *Living*, loose on the ground. I can only guess what it was that had caused the people around him to take notice. Maybe it was the newspaper slipping from his hands, and his not reaching to pick it back up.

My mother tried to avert three sets of eyes: mine, my brother's, and my sister's, but there was no way I wasn't going to look. I read about death all the time, and here it was, close. The man was a stranger, and his death provoked no emotion in me, so it was easy to gawk. When I started having sex a few years later, I would feel a similar way about my partners. I always felt the most comfortable having sex with people I felt nothing for.

Though he had probably died of a heart attack, or in some way clean of the violence New York City was famous for at the time, my mother still thought to herself that she'd made the right choice in leaving the city. When she had found out that she was pregnant with my older sister, she and my father had packed their bags and left.

But she still wanted us to have an appreciation, so a few times a year, we would go— Christmas, over February vacation, and in the summer. FAO Schwarz was the store I was always the most excited to visit, though we never bought anything. My mother would have to steal money from my dad's pants pockets in order to fund these trips. My parents hadn't spoken a word to each other for close to three years. Sometimes my father would leave notes in his pants pockets for my mother to find. "Stop thief!" one of them read, but my mom did not stop.

FAO Schwarz was a rich person's toy store and a poor person's tourist attraction. We went as tourists, to look at the Cabbage Patch Kid Village, and the piano that Tom Hanks danced on in *Big*. But the year I saw the dead man, I was 13, and my interests had started to change. The store I most wanted to visit was Trash and Vaudeville, in the East Village. It was the only store I knew of that sold punk rock t-shirts, spiky bracelets, and Doc Martens, items that were only mail-order accessible at the time, and required buying catalogs from ads that ran in the back of skateboarding magazines or *Rolling Stone* first. Not that my mother ever let me order any of those things. But trips to the city were considered special occasions, and at Trash and Vaudeville that morning, I had been able to convince her to let me buy a "Sid Lives" t-shirt with my Christmas money.

The world went on around the dead man. The subway platform became more densely populated with people waiting for the train.

"Are they just going to leave him?" my brother asked. He was nine, with a chubby face, and chunky body. *Husky* was what it said on the label inside of his pants. At home, he watched professional wrestling obsessively, one hand in a bowl of Doritos, the other gripping a Pepsi. He was the go-between in the communication of our parents, the tin can whenever it was absolutely necessary for them to play telephone. Precociously aware that much of what he needed to communicate for them was better off bowdlerized, he also acted as their censor, and translator. On the train into Grand Central, I had let him put me in a sleeper hold, and had passed out for a few seconds, drooling all over myself.

"They must be waiting for an ambulance," my mother said.

"Ambulance?" my sister interrupted. "He needs a body bag." She was fifteen, and held a shopping bag in her hand from The Strand. Inside were books by Henry Miller and D.H. Lawrence. It was because of her interest in infamous writers that we'd schlepped to the Chelsea Hotel that afternoon. At first I'd been resistant.

"You're such a poser," my sister said. "Nancy Spungen *died* there. I can't believe you don't want to go."

"That was the hotel?" I said. "I thought maybe it was a chain, like Howard Johnson's."

She was right. I was a poser. I'd write things in my journal like, "I'm not going to live 'til I'm 21," but had yet to do a thing that put my life in peril. She'd proven the point to me the week before. I had a Sid Vicious poster on the wall of our bedroom that read *Undermine their pompous authority, reject their moral standards, make anarchy and disorder your trademarks. Cause as much chaos and disruption as possible but don't let them take you alive.* After waking up to it so many mornings, I had the words memorized, and took the time necessary to write the voluble quote all over everything.

"I don't give a hoot, I'm dissolute," my sister wrote in the notebook that she kept next to her bed, and filled with quotations from books that she'd read and found to be meaningful. With a

jagged dash that looked like a lightning bolt on its side, she attributed the words to Sid. We snooped through each other's things all the time, and as soon as I'd read the quote, I began writing it everywhere, as she'd known that I would. Once I'd thoroughly saturated my life's tangible objects in the words, she told me the truth.

"Hahahahahaha!" she said. "If I just attach the right name to it, you'll recite it, dedicate your life to it. *I don't give a hoot! I'm dissolute!* You are *so* going to join a cult."

Policemen arrived on the platform. They marked a sloppy perimeter that cut across the plastic covering the man with yellow tape. *The Times* was picked up from the ground in front of him, and placed onto the bench.

"Bet that suit wasn't expecting to meet his maker today," a man said, standing somewhere near us on the platform. I turned towards his voice, but it was hard to get a good look at him. His features were completely obscured by the fur lined hood of his winter coat. "Dare you to touch 'em," he said. "You know you want to." He resembled a sort of faceless Eskimo.

"Stop staring, Fiona," my mom said.

"Do you think they're holding the subway 'til they move the body?" my brother asked. He had on his shit-face, the grimace he made whenever he was anxious, or had to use the bathroom.

"No, honey," my mother said. "They'd make some kind of announcement, if that was the case."

"If you're not going do it, I'm gonna do it," the man in the hood said. "I'm gonna tag that dead suit."

My mother's gestures tightened. It was rush hour, and trains continued to arrive on the station's other tracks. She moved the three of us into a tight group as the platform continued to fill with people. "Hold hands," she said. My sister and I ignored her.

"Don't be a puss," the man said. He towered above the other people on the platform, though he may have been standing on his tippy-toes. "Those cops?" his hood turned in the direction of where the closest police officers stood. There were only two in the area of the bench. "They ain't gonna stop you."

"I'm not going to tell you again, Fiona," my mother said.

There were so many things she didn't want me to see. Every homeless person. ACT-UP activists. Black Muslims. Packages of edible, strawberry and peach flavored underwear, at Trash and Vaudeville. A woman's exposed vagina, on a painting, in the lobby of the Chelsea. What was it about New York City that she wanted me to appreciate?

"Where do you think they get the plastic from?" my sister asked. "Do they just keep a roll of it down here, in a closet somewhere, in case someone dies?"

Before my mother could shush her, or in someway intimate that her words were aggravating my brother's nervous condition, a woman's static-heavy voice came over the speaker system.

"Due to an ongoing investigation, only the first five cars of the arriving uptown 6 train will be boarding at the platform."

"Last chance," the man in the hood said. "Go, go Godzilla."

"We have to move up," my mother said, sounding relieved.

"It's now or never," said the man. "Make your bones."

We had to walk past the bench. My mother looked at me, then my brother, and my sister. Her little ducks, we were all in a row.

She looped her arm around my brother's, like a vine. "Come on," she said. There were so many people on the platform, we would have to weave through them, in a formation that resembled a conga line.

One of the cops stood next to the garbage can, looking at something. The other had moved up the platform, and was refereeing a heated exchange between an Asian man and a white woman in a ratty fur coat. I put a few steps between me and sister fussing with my Trash and Vaudeville bag. I would use the garbage can as a cover, and feign throwing something away. I made a fist with my hand, as if there were something inside of it. My heart raced.

I could see the side of the man's face. Where the plastic touched his nose, it rose up, creating a gap. He was much younger than I had expected, maybe 40, or 50, and wore a pair of wire-rimmed glasses. I could see one tight, cork-screw sideburn. His mouth hung agape. "Agape" meant that God loved us. I had been taught this at C.C.D.

"Hey! What are you doing?" the police officer next to the garbage can said, finally looking up. I swung around, so I was facing him. "Use the can up the platform," he said.

"I'm sorry," I said, catching sight of what he had been looking at. It was the dead man's newspaper. It had been moved from the bench. He had been using the cover of the garbage can as a tabletop to support the paper as he flipped through it. He moved to throw it out.

"I'll take it," I said. "For my mom. For the train."

He pushed it towards me with a look of disdain. He didn't like that he'd been caught slacking on the job by a kid.

As if saying her name was a conjuring spell, my mother appeared at my side.

"I'm sorry ma'am," he said turning to her. Not deterred by her heavy sweater and winter coat, his eyes fixed on her chest. "We try to be fast, clean them up quick, but you know."

"What are you doing?" my mother said, without looking at him. She was exasperated. "Come on."

"I got you the paper," I said, but the sound of the subway entering the station made it hard to hear.

As the doors opened, I saw the man with the furry hood board. It was a miracle that the four of us got a seat, but we did, and he did, too. He sat across from us, and down a bit, but he was no longer interested in me. I tried to get his attention, waving the newspaper in his direction when my mother wasn't looking, but he kept his head down, and never looked up. If my mother had heard what I'd said about the paper being for her, she never asked me for it, and I didn't mention it again. When we got off the subway to transfer to the Metro North train that would take us the rest of the way home, I buried it in the bottom of my Trash and Vaudeville bag.

Three years later, when my father dropped dead of a heart attack while wobbly walking the line at a DWI checkpoint, his car, with the newspaper he'd bought that morning left on the back seat, would be towed back to our house. When no one was looking, I'd sneak out to the car, and grab the paper. I'd keep it as a souvenir, too.

Killing Michael J. Fox

In 1995, my mother was engaged to be married. As an ingratiating gesture, her fiancé offered to pay for me to go into drug treatment. The facility wasn't a rehab in the traditional, 30-day medical setting sense; it was a historical retreat within the AA community, the type of place program aficionados might go to recharge their spiritual batteries. It was expensive, but less costly than a thousands of dollars a month traditional facility. There was no detox there, so my family doctor wrote me a prescription for clonidine and a benzo, and the pills were dispensed to me my first week there by a nurse on staff. The place was quaint, out in the woods and rustic; there was a little chapel on the grounds and a garden where the patients could tend to plants and flowers. I was not interested in either spiritual matters or botanical ones, and as was the case with all my rehab experiences up to this point, I was the youngest person there. It was awkward being a drug addict in treatment at ages 17, 18, 19—I was still a kid, but was always placed with the adults, which just added to my sense of alienation. It was like being in treatment with your parents.

I became friendly with a woman there named Marci. She often treated me with a snobby sense of superiority, but because my outward appearance drew attention, and she liked attention, she decided to be my friend so we could share in the attention together. Instead of competing with me for it, we would divide and conquer. She was in her forties and wore cocktails dresses all the time, even when we went for walks in the woods, then she would swap her heels for sneakers. She had three children, and would dictate her letters to them to me and I would write them out for her. She would then take the letter to the administrative facility and photocopy it; ergo, each kid got the same letter.

On a regular, casual basis, I used to wear ripped fishnet stockings with shorts and skirts. One day, I wore fishnets to morning mediation and they caused a considerable stir amongst the patients and staff. I wasn't told *not* to wear them, but it was obvious it was a matter that we would be revisiting later. After the group, Marci begged me to take off the stockings, and let her wear them. I did, just to stop her pleading. Later that afternoon, we were both taken aside by the staff and told to retire the fishnets. Marci relished claiming that she was the reason the stockings had been banned, and recapping the incident for new patients. She seemed to think it implied something about her dangerous sexiness, as the stockings hadn't been banned until she put them on.

There was a large lodge on the grounds were they would hold AA meetings that were open to the public. Since the facility was storied in AA lore, people would come from far and wide and these meeting would be filled with hundreds of people. It was an exciting event for the patients. It was also the only time during the week we got to drink caffeinated coffee.

I grew up watching *Family Ties* and adored Michael J. Fox, whose real middle initial is the prescient "A," making his real name Michael A. Fox. *Back to the Future, Teen Wolf—* the precociously conservative Alex P. Keaton is still one of my favorite television characters. Fox has been candid in interviews about his struggles with alcoholism, and donates money to different causes connected with helping people get sober, so I don't feel I am "outing" him by writing this. I was outside the meeting lodge smoking a cigarette when he walked past me; I had to do a double take. I couldn't believe it. I was in the same immediate airspace as Marty fucking McFly. As awed as I was by this, I knew an AA meeting was not the place to approach him; after all, the second A in AA stands for *Anonymous*, and that dictate applies to celebrities, too. Marci appeared besides me dressed to the nines. I was literally so excited to see Michael J. Fox, I thought I might throw up.

"Michael J. Fox is here!" I whispered to her.

"What was he in again?" Marci asked. His name was familiar to her, but she couldn't recall any of his acting work; nonetheless she was clearly intrigued that there was a celebrity in our midst.

"We have to sit near him," she said, reading my mind. I figured this was ok, we could sit near him. What could be wrong with that? I wouldn't point, stare, or ogle him, but I would be close enough to note what kind of sneakers he had on, and this seemed like an important thing for me to know.

We settled into our seats a few rows behind him. I was content to just stare at the back of his head.

Marci suddenly jumped up.

"I'm going to say something to him," she said.

"No, don't!" I said, grabbing at the back of her dress, but it was too late. She went up to his chair in the next row and tapped him on his shoulder. He turned around to face her and she pointed in my direction.

"Will you say something to this girl?" she said confidently. "She's obsessed with you."

I wanted to die. I literally wanted to crawl under my chair and have the earth open and suck me inside of it. I could feel my face turning bright red, and when I saw the look on his face, I felt that I deserved to meet a painful end, too.

I spoke over Marci.

"No, no, it's ok! It's ok! I'm so sorry!"

Michael J. Fox glanced over in my direction. Then he gave Marci a look of pure poison, and turned back around. He never said a word, because he is a good actor, he didn't need to. With his face and body language, he had communicated exactly how he felt about us.

Since Michael J. Fox did not try to flirt with her and she couldn't engage him, all that was left for Marci to do was come back to her seat and sit down. "I tried!" she said loudly, as if to re-inforce that I'd put her up to it.

A few minutes later, the meeting began. At the start of the discussion part, Michael J. Fox got up and left. I felt horrible. I felt like the biggest, tackiest, douchiest loser in the world. Later, when I got back to my room and told my roommate what had happened, she made me feel worse: What if Michael J. Fox had been thinking about drinking, she said, and because we had made him feel so uncomfortable that he'd left the meeting, he went on a bender on his way home?

In essence she was saying to me, what if you just *killed* Michael J. Fox?

I hated Marci for what she had done. I never wanted to talk to her ever again.

Thankfully, the next week, a man named Tyler checked himself into the program and rescued me from her clutches. He had a lazy eye and wore Hootie and The Blowfish t-shirts. It took about a week and a half, but I fell in rehab love.

Love.

Try as they might, it's the one drug no rehab can keep off their grounds.

The Optimism of Being a Dope Fiend

I remember clearly the first time my best friend Chelsea and I decided to play at prostitution. I say *play* because even though we were most definitely trading sex for goods and worldly services, that's what it felt like, play. Almost anything can feel like play when done amongst friends, drunken orgies of unprotected sex, intravenous drug use, even a violent criminal act like a pushing a hippy from a moving Volkswagen bus to steal his shrooms. It's the transformative power of the laugh track of friendship; it's also the soundtrack to a sort of shared madness.

We kept our client list small. It consisted of only one very preferred customer, our good friend, Chris, whom both of us had already had sex with anyway. So, really, it just seemed like mixing things up a bit, taking something that was normal and natural and sticking a price tag on it. Our first foray into prostitution was very much like the buying and selling of pet rocks.

Surprisingly, Chris wasn't resistant to the idea at all; on the contrary, it excited him. It was obvious he got off on the sleaziness of the concept as much as I did. The world of vice and sexual debauchery had always held an attraction for me. At seventeen, I viewed it as this parallel universe where anything went, free of the glaring lights of society's judgment. I just lacked an in.

Once the plan was in place, Chris had a hard time controlling his anticipation, covertly grabbing my ass as we passed each other in the hallway or tonguing the V between his pointer and middle finger when our eyes met on the lunch line. We'd been having sex on and off for years, but this unexpected dash of *quid pro quo* was adding a spicy new ingredient to our bromidic old recipe. Maybe it was because Chris was incredibly good-looking and willing females just threw themselves at him. The idea that someone was actually saying *if you want it, you have to pay for it*, turned him on.

The currency in exchange for the sex would be drugs. Once our end of the deal was satiated, Chris would drive Chelsea and me a half hour to East Haven and buy us heroin, which we had started doing about six months earlier. I was a high school senior and Chelsea was a sixteen-year-old correspondence-schooled junior. Neither of us had jobs and neither of us drove, so this arrangement with Chris would gratify all that we desired but lacked in one fell swoop.

Arriving at my house after school, I told Chris to take off all his clothes and wait for me in my bedroom. I went into my sister's room and rifled through her underwear drawer, grabbing the short baby blue negligee she always wore after bathing. Figuring myself properly garbed, I returned to the bedroom where Chris was sitting on the edge of the bed in his boxer shorts. He acknowledged my return with a nervous laugh.

"Put the money on the bedside table, big boy," I said lifting his legs onto the mattress and pushing his body down onto the bed with my own. I then slid into a straddle over his now prone form.

The usual nerves I felt before sex quickly dissipated as I outwardly affected the personality traits I imagined to be the hallmarks of any good prostitute's identity—confidence and control. In Alcoholics Anonymous, they say *Fake It 'Til You Make It* and that's what I was doing. Focusing on the character I was creating allowed me to forget who I really was, an insecure high school senior who usually asked Chris to turn off the lights before we screwed. Also, even though I knew most guys would fuck just about anything, something about a guy paying for sex said to me he must really want it, and want it from *me* the person he was paying. I found this validation via capitalism to be incredibly flattering.

I slid a condom over Chris's cock and spun around on my hands and knees, my ass now square with his eye line.

"You want some of this, big boy?" I said pulling up the back of my negligee like a curtain rising on a movie screen.

I didn't need to repeat the question. Chris grabbed me tightly by my hips and we were finished with two quick jabs from behind.

After Chelsea took her turn, which took a little bit longer due to a necessary post-coitus recuperation period, we went to East Haven, copped a few bags of dope each and returned to our respective homes.

I was so happy and high I decided to actually do my homework.

***

A few days later, I called Chelsea from school during my lunch break. She had dropped out of school earlier in the year. Just barely ascending to her junior year, her parents had decided to let her take classes through a correspondence school in the hopes of getting her diploma. Since they worked, this meant Chelsea would be home alone all day, waiting for her assignments to come in the mail. Free of parental interference, her family's large home had morphed into the go-to destination for area school-skippers.

"Hey," she said. "Make sure to come by later. I'm going to have a present for you."

"*Present?*" I repeated, my stomach flip-flopping with nervous anticipation. Her phraseology could be indicative of only one thing. Or more than one thing, all of the same family of illicit substances.

"Anthony's here," she continued. "He's going to give me some pills."

Anthony Francessi was a boy in my grade. He had been born with a hare lip and in middle school would insert spaghetti up his nose and pull it out the hole in the top of his mouth to make friends. He'd had many surgeries to correct it but none had done much good, only adding to the layers of deep scarring that covered the area from the middle of his nose to the top of his lips. What surgeons hadn't been able to fix on his face, Anthony tried to compensate for with his body, at the gym. He had an athlete's physique that always got him named *Best Body* in our class's yearbook superlatives. He was a peripheral person in our world, a jock whereas Chelsea and I were into punk rock. But in a town as small as ours was, there were no cliquish rivalries and diverging interests existed side by side. They had to; otherwise, if you had a party there would only be about five people to invite.

"*Give* you some pills?" I asked. Anthony had never struck me as the overtly generous type.

"Well, I'm going to blow him for them," Chelsea responded.

"Chelsea!" I said, taken aback by her casual bravado. "How did this arrangement even come about?" Our dalliance with Chris had been between the three of us, though we hadn't come up with any rules or perimeters pertaining to an explanation to the outside world. Chris had a steady girlfriend, so the assumption had been that we would all just keep our mouths shut but see each other again when needs and wants arose.

"I don't have any money, so I just offered," she answered.

"*Okay*," I said, surprised that Chelsea was actually running with the barter system and offering it freely to others.

I felt uneasy and reviewed my hesitations. Yes, Anthony was our friend but the relationship didn't have nearly the same years of foundation and trust as our relationship with Chris. But like Joan Jett, neither Chelsea nor I gave a damn about our bad reputations. We actually considered it sport to annihilate whatever positive was left of them. We wrote graffiti about ourselves in the school bathrooms and made out with each other in the hallways. I had pushed a planning room teacher and hung a paper mache version of the principal in effigy in the hallway. But Chelsea wasn't attending public high school anymore. If Anthony decided to talk shit, Chelsea was beyond the reach of his words. And I could always stick up for her and say he was full of shit.

"Ok Chelsea," I said. "Whatever you want to do. I'll see you in a little while."

At the end of the school day, I got a ride to her house. I was surprised when I saw no cars in the driveway, anticipating evidence of a shindig in full swing. I went around the back and entered through the open door on the porch. Music was blaring from the back hallway. Chelsea's parent's house was as long as it was wide, her bedroom so far from the house's main rooms of activity one had to wonder if her existence was being purposely hidden from view. I followed the music back to her bedroom and entered. Though it was only mid-afternoon and the sun was still high in the sky, all the shades had been drawn and the room was completely dark. In spite of the absence of light, I could still make out Chelsea's outline on the bed.

"Chelsea?" I said, unable to hear my own voice over the music. The ambiance of the room and her perfectly laid out form on the bed made me think of a headbanger's wake. "I'm going to turn this off," I screamed. As I turned off the music, I flipped on the light.

"Are you ok?" I asked. The thought went through my mind that maybe she had been unable to wait for my arrival and had taken all of Anthony's pills herself.

"Yes," she answered, just as I noticed her eyebrows. Fresh dots of blood lined her browline where the hairs had been yanked out at the root. Savaging her eyebrows was Chelsea's primary nervous release; she usually concealed the damage with an eyebrow pencil and powder. I had never seen the aftermath so fresh and forthright.

"Anthony's not back yet?" she asked.

"Back yet?" I repeated.

"He had to go and get the pills," she replied.

"Go and *get* the pills? How long ago was this? When did he leave?"

Chelsea got up and began to pace the room in terse zig zags, stopping in front of the stereo.

"Please don't turn it on," I begged. As I spoke, I surveyed the room. Chelsea's bra was on the floor near the bed and the garbage can next to it was filled with wadded-up balls of tissue.

"I hate that fucker," she spat, finally. "He ripped me off. He fucking ripped me off. I stuck his fucking cock in my mouth and he fucking ripped me off."

She picked up a heavy wooden jewelry box and heaved it against the wall. The jewelry inside scattered all over the carpet, though the box itself did not break. From the mass of tangled cords and ornaments she picked up a Misfit's *Fiend Club* necklace and wrapped its chain tightly around her fingers.

"It was so gross. Of course he couldn't cum. He kept making this sound, this laugh. *Huh-huh-huh-huh.* Like *Beavis and Butthead.* And then he said, 'Take your shirt off, I'll cum faster if you take it off.' Like he was the one calling the shots, like he was the one in control. But I figured, *ok*, I just wanted it to be over. Then he said, 'Take your pants off, I want to see your pussy. Seeing your pussy will make me cum.' And all his friends were hooting and hollering outside the door. But I would not fucking kiss him. I would not touch that scarred lump he pretends is a mouth with my lips."

She stopped for a moment and I knew she was thinking about how she could destroy the necklace in her hands. She put it down.

"And just so you know, his body is not as fucking great as everyone thinks it is."

"Oh Chelsea," I said, putting my arms around her shoulders.

"I'm not done yet. Oh no. It gets better. He came in my mouth. I feel so dumb. So fucking dumb. And then he tells me he has to go and *get* the pills. I don't know why I didn't ask for them first...and as he's putting his pants on, I'm thinking to myself, I bet this fucker is going to rip me off. And I just gave him something I can never, ever get back."

"He wouldn't do that to you," I spoke quickly and unconvincingly as the anger I felt made my voice quiver. "He knows we'd fucking kill him. Something happened and it's just taking him awhile. Here, let's call him on the phone," I grabbed for its cradle next to the bed.

"There were never any fucking pills. You know he's always been a huge liar. This was all a big joke to him. Call him though. Go ahead. I want to see what the fucker has to say."

I didn't know Anthony's phone number, so I called information. As the only Francessis in town, it wasn't difficult to unearth. His grandmother, the live-in matriarch of his large Italian family, answered on the first ring.

"Is Anthony there?" I asked.

"He's sleeping," she replied.

"He's sleeping?"

I silently implored the old woman to go and check.

"Makes sense," Chelsea said, standing close enough to hear the exchange. "The fucker blew his load and now he's taking a nap." She grabbed the phone from my hand.

"Hello," she said into the mouthpiece. "If I heard you right, Anthony's sleeping? Could you give him a message for me? And I don't need to tell you who this is, because Anthony will know. Could you tell him that the next time I see him, could you tell him that the next time I see him I'm gonna cut off his cock and make him floss with it, I'm gonna cut off his cock and stick in that hole that goes from his nose to mouth..."

She slammed down the phone and supported herself with her arms on the table.

"I really want to get high," she said. "How can we get some money?"

I had nothing to propose. It seemed crass to suggest Chris.

"You know, I noticed a phone number on that lock on the chest my parents put the change jar in," Chelsea said. Her parents had kept a huge change jar in their living room, a change jar as big as the house they lived in, as big as their bulging bank accounts. Once we started raiding it regularly, they had moved it to an old steamer trunk in their bedroom and affixed the trunk with a large combination padlock.

Chelsea continued, "Maybe if we call the phone number on the back of the lock and tell them some bullshit story about our kid locking the cat inside the trunk they'll give us the combination."

About an hour later, we had close to a hundred dollars in quarters. Unable to find a ride to East Haven, I agreed to skip school the next day and take the train there with her, after cashing in the quarters at the supermarket.

***

After 8 AM, the commuter railroad made only sporadic trips to New Haven, so we really had no choice but to take the train in at that early hour. We wouldn't have been able to just sit and stew at Chelsea's house anyway. It had started to rain just as we boarded the train and by the time we arrived at our destination it was pouring. The weather dovetailed perfectly with our moods.

Chelsea wasn't saying much. Familiar with her process for dealing with things that bothered her, I didn't pester her to talk. I didn't want to think about what had happened either. Anthony and I had classes together and I didn't know what I would do the next time I saw him. I assumed it would involve violence. There was a part of me that felt responsible for what had occurred. The arrangement with Chris, the arrangement that had given Chelsea the idea to proposition Anthony in the first place, had been my idea. I also knew that she had been hoping to impress me by coming up with a similar arrangement with Anthony, all on her own.

Since we were still new to the heroin game, we didn't have a large, rotating stable of drug dealer's phone numbers to call. Of the ones we did have, no one was answering the phone so early in the morning. The anxiety we felt had an undercurrent of electricity to it and we had to move. After twenty minutes of trying to call the numbers we had without success, we decided to walk into East Haven and cop off the street. It was something we had done before.

Before we set out, we spent five dollars on an umbrella from the newspaper stand inside the train station. It was the only one left in the bin and made for a child, printed with the same repeating graphic of an elephant in raingear frolicking happily in a puddle. The umbrella, along with the cost of our train tickets to New Haven and back, brought our original $100 down to about $70.

We walked for over an hour in silence, both of us lost in our own thoughts and revenge fantasies. The streets were mostly empty, the rain keeping everyone but the most desperate inside.

There is a non-verbal language that transpires between drug user and seller when copping on the street, a series of glances shot back and forth that convey interest and intent. It is necessary to give off these looks to unmask dealers, and them, customers, in otherwise anonymous passersby. It was getting ridiculous constantly moving the umbrella up and down to show off our faces whenever a person passed or a car drove by so we finally just put the umbrella down and got soaked instead. The situation was getting dire when a bus stop awning appeared like a mirage. We had circled the block several times without noticing it. Now we ran to it and sat down.

The barrage of rainwater we'd been exposed to had loosened the fresh scabs on Chelsea's browline. She had removed even more phantom hairs since I'd seen her the day before. Because the hair that she was so savaging was long lost to other ravages, what she was plucking was her own skin. Streaks of blood, like deluded watercolor paint ran the distance between her brow and eyelid. It pooled on her lids like a pale pink liquid eye shadow.

A bus pulled in and two young Hispanic men got off. We were two young, white, punk rock girls in a completely black and Spanish neighborhood. It was obvious what we were up to. We'd been relying on that obviousness since we'd left the train station. It had made up the backbone of our copping strategy.

"What you need, mommy?" the bigger of the two men asked.

"Dope," I answered.

You reach a point when trying to cop unsuccessfully where you know there's a high likelihood that the option placed in front of you won't work out, but because there are no other options, you take it anyway. A risky choice is better than no choice at all. There is optimism to being a dope fiend that you hang onto until it is taken from you. An optimism that you hold on to so tightly it must be snatched from your hands.

"How many you need?" he asked.

"Six," I answered.

As soon as the number was out of my mouth, I knew I shouldn't have said as much. Uncomfort and exhaustion had clouded my street smarts. I had wanted it to be over, but not like this.

"Give me the money," he said. "I'll go get for you."

"No," I answered.

I looked over at Chelsea. Her eyes were two big black moons.

"All right ladies, I tried playing nice with you," the bigger man said, reaching into his pocket and pulling out a medium-sized knife. "I don't feel like playing nice with you no more."

"You bitches be stupid for even coming down here," the littler one said, turning to watch his friend as he slid our $70 into his pocket. "Look at their dumb-ass umbrella," he pointed to our rain covering and its happy, frolicking elephants. "Like stealing candy from a baby."

"Or a blowjob from a prostitute," Chelsea whispered, the pink above her eyelids descending down her cheeks as she brought her hands to her face and began to cry.

Pray to St. Anthony

"What about arson? Fire. Have you ever purposely lit a fire?

"No...no! I mean, not purposely. Well, once, maybe. I was drunk and I wasn't thinking straight. I would have never, ever done it had I not been drunk."

"Why did you do it?"

"To get a guy's attention. We were both drunk, and he passed out. I wanted to have sex, and he wouldn't wake up. I felt ignored. I wasn't trying to hurt him. I was just being dramatic. I wanted his attention."

"So, just that one time, when you were being, in your words, 'dramatic'?"

"Yes, but like I said, my intent wasn't malicious. I didn't want to hurt him, and I didn't."

"How did he react?"

"He got pissed! I lit the blanket he was sleeping under. It was a blanket his grandmother had made for him, and he took my arms, and he used my arms to put out the fire."

"Um...*okay*. What about animals? Have you ever purposely harmed an animal?"

"No! And I know where you're going with this. I've read enough books to know. You're going down that sociopathy checklist. I've never harmed any animal. I've always loved animals. I even volunteered at the pound when I was a kid. Wow, I actually haven't thought about that in years."

"What?"

"Well, there was this one time, at the pound. A friend and I, we volunteered there together. The woman who worked there, who gave us our duties...I can see her in my mind. Then I didn't know it, but now I can see that she was a dyke, a lesbian. A real lumber jack lesbian. She had big, thick glasses. Her hair was short on the sides, and long in the back, going down into a rat's tail. She always wore a really heavy L.L. Bean-type workman's shirt. She wasn't very nice to us. We were volunteering, but you could tell she didn't want us there, that she thought we were in the way. So, she had us in this back room, cleaning shit-strewn cages, changing the newspapers, and my friend and I, we were kind of stewing, because we could tell she didn't like us, and we wanted to be doing something else, like walking the dogs, something that wasn't so gross and manual. So, we started making fun of the lady, and I took the clip out of my hair, to pretend I had a mullet, and for some reason, I put it on this cat's tail. I don't know why I did it. The cat went *crazy*. He was jumping all over the room, knocking things over, just going nuts, and we couldn't get him to stay still long enough so we could get the clip off of him. He looked like a cat in a cartoon who'd been electrocuted, like he should have had big 3-D letters underneath him that said ZAPPED! So we knew we were in big trouble now, I mean the evidence was on this cat's tail, and the room was a mess, and all of the other animals were going crazy, because the cat was freaking out. My friend and I just looked at each other. Then the woman came into the room yelling, "What's going on in here?" and we just barreled right past her, almost knocking her over, and out the door. We ran all the way home."

"Was there any consequence?"

"Well, this is the weird part. To volunteer, we had to fill out these forms, with our names, addresses, phone numbers. So I was expecting a call. And then I got home, and nothing. My mother didn't say a word. But later that week, I see my hairclip on the counter in the kitchen. I felt like I'd been punched in the stomach. My mom hadn't said anything, so I asked her, "Mom, where did you get this hairclip? I thought I'd lost it." And she says, and you have to understand, my mother is really very square, very Christian, she says, "Well dear, St. Anthony must be on your side because it came back to you. I found it out in the mailbox."

Captain Save-A-Ho

I never know what to say when I'm asked if I knew anyone who died on September 11th. It's a conflict that cuts right to the strange nature of sex work—the intimate anonymity, the intimate indifference. I could be standing in front of a client's name on the Memorial Wall at Ground Zero and never know it, because I never learned his last name or had long since forgotten it.

I'm pretty sure Stephen died on September 11th. He worked at Cantor Fitzgerald, a company located on floors 101-105 of Tower 1. Most of the 658 employees in those offices that morning died in the attacks. I was seeing Stephen two to three times a month through the outcall escort agency I worked for in New York City, and after August of 2001, I never saw him again.

I met Stephen at a bachelor party. I hated bachelor parties. I hated them because the elements that made them such a good time for the men in attendance—the randy women, the booze, the feeling of brotherhood—conspired to bring out something ugly in them: bravado.

This particular bachelor party immediately got off to a bad start. A friend of the groom called the woman I was doing the party with—a voluptuous Latina in a platinum blonde wig who went by the name Moet—"hefty," and she freaked out, storming off to find the friend of the groom who had set up the party, demanding an apology before she would perform. The party was held inside some kind of shipping/receiving warehouse in Manhattan, and I didn't know Moet at all. I had met her just minutes before outside the warehouse, and when she stormed off, I assumed she had left me. Standing there all by myself in a transparent slip dress and heels, I felt like carrion for a pack of hungry wolves.

"How much for a blowjob?" one man barked.

"Will you let me snort coke off your ass?" asked another.

"You and the fat one—you eat her pussy?" inquired a third.

To make matters worse, I wasn't much of a dancer. I had tried stripping once, and hated it; I found my fit in sex work that was much more one-on-one, much less all-eyes-on-me. Though most of the other escorts at the agency liked doing bachelor parties because of the tips and party atmosphere, I avoided them, viewing them as frat parties for grown men. The only reason I agreed to do this one was the soothing words of the phone girl: It was only a few guys, she swore. It was hastily organized, not even a real bachelor party, more of a last-minute cap on the night's festivities. From their voices on the phone, they sounded so drunk, she doubted they would be standing up. And Moet—bachelor parties were her forte. She was a pro.

But now I was Moet-less, flanked by a group of at least ten men and counting, all of whom stood upright and alert, except for the guys sitting in the circle of foldout chairs in the center of the room. The phone girl's assurances had obviously been a con job, tailored to placate my insecurities. The men had probably requested a white girl for the party, and I was the only one available. Though confident I could handle the situation, I felt vulnerable and extremely uncomfortable, the primary reasons I chose to avoid bachelor parties in the first place.

"Hey, I got an idea!" a man called out from behind a large desk in a corner of the room. "Let's all play strip poker!"

"Shut up, Steve!" a sweaty man in a suit jacket whined. Most of the men where clad in subtle variations of the same ensemble: pants and suit jackets that had probably appeared much nattier earlier in the evening. "Come sit on my lap, baby, and rub those titties all over me. I know you've got some great titties under that dress," the sweaty man beckoned, crooking his finger in a come-hither motion in my direction.

"That's not fair, Ray!" the man behind the desk scolded, standing up. He looked to be about fifty, with a paunchy stomach and khaki pants worn high on his waist. He took off his suit jacket and draped it on the back of his chair dramatically, a la Demi Moore in *Striptease*. "Why should she be the only one who takes her clothes off?" he said, jiggling his big belly and unbuttoning his shirt to an imaginary beat.

"I don't know, Steve, maybe because she's a *stripper?*" a voice in the group growled.

The man with the large belly opened a drawer of the desk and gestured towards me. "We have our company poker night here," he said. He reached into the desk drawer and pulled out a basket filled with unopened card decks. "You know how to play?" he asked.

I shook my head no.

"I'll show ya," he answered with a wink, handing me an unopened deck. He lowered his voice, and I leaned in closer to hear him. "It's been a *looooong* night, hon. We're just getting back from the casino, and I'm pretty sure the groom's puking in another room. Everyone here's nice, just wasted. Just do your thing, hon.

These," he indicted towards the cards, "should keep the heat off of you a little bit."

"Let's play STRIP POKER!" he yelled out, rolling his belly and wiggling his hips as he threw the card decks to the men in all directions. "I can't wait to see what you're working with, Hector!"

In light of Moet's MIA status, the man's gesture made me feel like I had an ally, though one could never be sure in this business. As the men grumbled to themselves and dodged the flying card decks, I moved to the center of the circle of chairs, ready to start my slow, drawn-out removal of garments. There was no music, so the men's obnoxious inquiries and demands would have to serve as my soundtrack. Suddenly, Moet burst back into the room, the groom, supported by the best man, following behind her.

"Come on now, Kenny," the best man slurred. "You have to apologize to this lovely lady! Look at those lips! She could suck the chrome off a bumper!" He had lipstick on both sides of his face and wobbled on his feet. His fly was partially unzipped, and I could make out the tartan plaid of his boxer shorts through the opening.

"I never said anything to her, Mike, I swear," Kenny stammered. "It was all a misunderstanding. I was asking for a Hefty bag, for the beer cans..."

"Well, she's ready to show us all a good time, but only if you say those two magic words. Otherwise, she's out of here, and it's going to be all your fault. Right, Moet?"

Moet appeared to be in much better spirits upon reentering the room, and was wearing a man's tie around her neck, its knot perfectly aligned with the ample swell of her cleavage. Her spandex minidress looked to be at least three sizes too small and barely touched the tops of her meaty thighs. She marched over to Kenny, a slight man with feminine features and large glasses that threatened to overwhelm his face, and straddled his lap.

"Do I feel heavy to you, baby?" she purred, her large posterior extending far past his knees.

"No, baby, no! You feel just right!" Kenny said, his voice going up a few octaves as his small frame was engulfed by so much Moet.

The best man looked at me. "You gonna show us a good time, too, Courtney?"

I opened my mouth to speak with my best feigned enthusiasm, but the man with the large belly cut me off.

"I was kind of hoping Courtney and I could be alone, Mike."

Moet gyrated deeper into the lap of the man who had insulted her. The best man surveyed the room, his eyes stopping to linger on Moet. Based on her performance, he must have decided mine wouldn't be necessary.

"Alright Steve-o, she's yours, but you owe me. You can take her into that room in the back."

Another thing I didn't particularly enjoy about bachelor parties were these public negotiations of my services that didn't involve me.

I picked up my bag from a chair and waited for the man to lead me towards the back room, but he just stood there, looking at me impatiently.

"What's the matter?" I asked.

"You're forgetting your cards, hon. You want to learn, right?"

I looked over at Moet, in an attempt to communicate to her where I was going, but I couldn't get her attention. She was bent over Kenny's chair as if doing a backbend, her arms on both sides of his lap, and her breasts upside down in his face.

It was the one thing about the bachelor party the phone girl hadn't lied about.

Moet *was* a pro.

Stephen and I sat in the back room for the next hour and half playing strip poker for prudes. He didn't want me to take off anything beyond my bra and panties. All that left me to remove was my dress and shoes. He stayed in his boxer shorts.

"Thanks," I said, acknowledging the diversion he'd created in the other room. "But you didn't have to do that. I've done plenty of bachelor parties."

"I saw your eyes," he said. "You looked like a deer in the head-lights of life. Moet doesn't have that look." He ashed his cigarette into a plastic cup of beer. "I wouldn't have been able to live with myself. I can't get off on that. My name's Stephen, but I also have a superhero alter ego. They call me Captain Save-A-Ho."

I laughed, even though he was calling me a ho.

All of the men at the bachelor party that night, except for the groom's best man, whom it was mentioned he had known since childhood, worked at Cantor Fitzgerald, in Tower 1 of the World Trade Center.

***

The phone girl told me that Stephen had called every night since the party to see if I was working. A few nights later, I was, and I was driven to his Brooklyn Heights Brownstone. Five years before, he told me, he had split up with his wife who was living on Long Island with their teenage daughter. We went into his bedroom, and he reached into a dresser drawer and took out a small bag of white powder.

"I got this the other night at the casino," he said. "Bought it in the parking lot. I'm not really sure why. It's not my thing."

I cut a line of it on top of the table next to his bed. Its consistency was both soft and crunchy, like some kind of salt mixed with soap. I blew it behind the bed when he wasn't looking. I didn't have the heart to tell him it was fake.

We had sex and his sweat rained down on me in salty droplets. His breathing quickly became labored.

"I wish you could have seen me in my prime, Courtney," he said. "Wait." He ran into another room and came back with a photo album. There were pictures of him from high school playing football, pictures from what looked to be a college frat party; it made me think of the bachelor party at the warehouse. "After your forties, hon, it's all downhill," he said. "But it was a great ride."

As I was leaving, he tipped me a hundred dollars, then made an all too familiar request.

"Give me your phone number, hon," he said. "We can cut the agency right out of it."

I'd been down that road a million times before and had learned the hard way that unless you had some kind of special line just for them, it never paid to give a client your phone number. It ended up abused, treated like a free phone-sex line or a drunken confessional. So I compromised and gave Stephen my new email address.

My mother had just bought two computers she'd seen advertised on television and gave me one as a gift. It wasn't exactly a *real* computer—it was called an i-Opener, and it was similar to WebTV in that it was just the Internet, a keyboard, and a screen. Because my i-Opener had been a present from my mom, it was registered through her account, and my email address had one very small difference from hers: the number 1.

As I wrote down my email address for Stephen, I stressed the importance of remembering this digit.

"Don't forget the 1," I said.

"No worries, hon," he replied.

He forgot the 1 and emailed my mom.

***

As a sex worker, there are three questions you are asked constantly by clients. The first one is "What's your real name?" Clients are obsessed with this question. If they can get you to tell them your real name, it makes them feel special, elevated. The relationship is still a paid one, but now they know you just as anyone who is important to you in your other life does. Disclosing your name also negates what may be the most important veneer a sex worker has: anonymity. It's a revelation that can be interpreted to imply, "She either trusts me enough not to call out to her if I were to see her on the street, or she actually wants me to come up to her and say hello." The second question clients always ask is "What were the circumstances that led you to sex work?" or, as they see it, the circumstances that led you astray, from good girl to bad. The third question is "What gets you off sexually?" This is usually phrased as "Now tell me what *you* like."

I never told Stephen my real name. It was nothing against him. I had told other clients my name in the past, but because "Fiona" came across as more exotic-sounding than "Courtney," before the movie *Shrek* at least, to them it sounded like even *more* of a stripper name, and they never believed me. So I told Stephen that Courtney *was* my real name, that in spite of what he may have believed as Captain Save-A-Ho, there was nothing to save me from—my private life and public life blurred together. So when Stephen emailed my mother, he addressed the email in part to Courtney.

My mother had gotten other emails meant for me after buying me the i-Opener, but nothing related to sex work. Thankfully, Stephen hadn't written anything too revealing, just that he would like to see me again soon and had enjoyed our time together. My mother probably wouldn't have even thought the email was meant for me if Stephen hadn't addressed it not just to "Courtney" but to "Courtney Love." He was being funny, but I was a big fan of hers, and my mother knew this.

In January of 2002, I was living with my mom and using her i-Opener when I came across Stephen's email, then six months old. My exit from New York City had happened hastily the previous December when I had lost my apartment in a perfect storm of Xanax addiction and unpaid rent. Clients come and go from your life—your life and theirs mix in hour-long intervals and dollar allotments, and it occurred to me as I read Stephen's email that I couldn't recall seeing him after August of the previous summer.

I wrote down his email address, logged into my newly created Yahoo email account and wrote:

Stephen—

It's Courtney. Sorry I didn't get in touch sooner, but everything's just been so crazy the last few months. I can't imagine what it's been like for you. The loss of life is staggering. I don't want to say too much now, I'd rather wait for you to respond first, but I'm no longer in New York. Hopefully I'll be back soon. Just wanted to make sure you're okay and let you know I'm thinking about you.

Just as I was about to hit send, it occurred to me that my new email address might cause some confusion. It contained my real name, Fiona, followed by some numbers that were relevant to my life. I'd been so adamant to Stephen about Courtney being my real name that I figured it warranted some kind of passing explanation.

This is my new email address, I added. *Fiona's my real name. I was just trying to keep some distance, you know?*

***

I did make it back to New York, and in the summer of 2002, I found myself working for the same outcall escort agency I'd been working for when I met Stephen. One night, my driver for the evening took me to meet a friend of his, another driver for the agency, between calls. I recognized the girl his friend was driving for the night immediately: the big breasts, the wide, shapely hips. The only thing different about her was the sable color of her wig. It was Moet.

"I remember you," she said, getting out of the car to smoke a cigarette and empty the sand from her shoes. Her driver had just picked her up from a call she had done at the beach. "We did that bachelor party together, and you ditched me."

"I didn't ditch you!" I said defensively. I had experienced the brunt end of other girls' reactions to imagined crimes in the past.

"Relax, mami," she said. "You remembered where those guys worked, didn't you? That company, in the Towers? What's your name again, mami?"

"Courtney."

"People can say whatever they want about us and what we do, Courtney, but those men that night, they didn't have much time left. And maybe I'm crazy for even thinking like this, but that night I know I showed them a good time, and they went home happy. Do you know what I mean, mami? I gave them my all that night, and I feel good about that."

Joan Vollmer Burroughs Died for Somebody's Sins not Mine

Here's the thing. I am very distrustful. I've been burned many times. One time in particular that was quite painful was by Patti Smith. She was with her then boyfriend, the young man who would go on to become the photographer, who would be wearing monogrammed slippers in fifteen years time, shooting flowers and whips up his asshole. A good looking fellow with unkempt curls. Bill would not have cruised him as he liked Spaniards.

They were at the Chelsea Hotel, what we used to call the *Literary Leper Colony* as a kick. Not out of disrespect for the address but because so many of the greats had gone there to die. Patti was very aware of the anniversary, she'd even found out approximate times from somewhere, though she and the boy did travel in the same loose circles as Bill when he was in town. They had dressed for their parts, the boy in a handsome Salvation Army suit coat and matching pants and Patti in a diaphanous slip dress and pearlescent shawl. There's not much written as to my sartorial flair. Despite having such a prolific circle of writers for friends, it's amazing how invisible I have remained. It was because of this that when dressing as me Patti defaulted her look to that of Ophelia before hitting the brook.

At 7:15 PM, Patti and the boy exchanged words like they imagined Bill and I might have before I was shot. So much pageantry was involved in their reenactment it's a wonder they didn't sell tickets. It was like a warped wedding ceremony, the groom being artistic sensibility. *We now pronounce ourselves outlaw artistes!*

"I think it's time for our William Tell Act," the young man said without emotion.

"I don't think I can look, you know how I can't stand the sight of blood," Patti replied.

The only aspect of the recreation they'd neglected was the weaponry. Instead of a .38 the boy had a small plastic water gun, painted brown and filled with red food coloring. He put a tumbler glass onto her head and backed up not too far. I saw something in his face, it read like hesitancy. A squirt of food coloring hit her squarely between the eyes. She twitched and the glass fell without breaking. As the pinkish-red trail ran down her forehead she collapsed to the floor.

Finé.

The whole thing was really a rather crass affair, but who's to say, I might be biased. My husband and I have become one of the most popular his and hers Halloween costumes in certain circles of New York. More popular then Zelda and Scott, at least as popular as June and Henry. I'd seen my share of these farbs but Patti's was the first by a person in circumstances similar to my own and with a connection. I suppose it was the reason I was drawn out. That and it was obvious she was *outré* enough not to be completely spooked by the idea of talking to a ghost.

She dropped to the floor, feigning the last wheezy breaths of my death's rattle. The boy waited a few seconds before leaning down and helping her to her feet. She moved her hand to his face as he lifted her, to caress his smooth skin and invite him to kiss her. Instead he moved her hand away.

"I have to go," he said. This *going* of his had become a reoccurring motif. Though he was rejecting her advances, it was not with cruelty.

"Where?" she asked. The food coloring had streaked down her forehead and pooled at the bridge of her nose. Her costuming was in such stark contrast to the boy's. He looked debonair, brashly handsome; with the blood, she looked like a Bellevue escapee.

"To Terry's loft..."

"You spend more time with Terry than you do with me, Robert. Not a small feat considering we live together."

"I said I'd do this with you..." He moved his hands in the air, though the fleeting traces of their reenactment. "I don't want to argue. He's waiting for me. I'll be back later tonight, I promise."

Once the boy had gone, she went over to the bookcase and took out a small, elegantly constructed handmade diary. She poured herself a glass of wine from the bottle she had planned to use as an aid in the seduction of the boy, if only she had made it that far.

She picked up a pen, sat down at a small table and began to write: *Rimbaud, Whitman, Blake, Burroughs: Robert and I are similar in the way we express our idolatry. We commune with our influences; covet their experiences like cicerones to luminosity. But it appears for Robert having one such experience Rimbaudesque hasn't been enough. Jim Carroll said he knew he wasn't gay because he only did it with men for money. I'm fairly certain that Robert is now doing it with them for free.*

Without confirmation from the boy she was in purgatory. Without confirmation as to the circumstances of my death, I was too. You could say I thought we could help each other out of a jam.

Not wanting to scare her but conceding that some fright was inevitable, I waited 'til she had finished her first glass of wine and had the beginnings of a glow on. When she got up to use the bathroom in the hallway, engaging all three door locks behind her, I even refilled her glass to encourage more consumption.

There was so much riff-raff in the halls of the Chelsea that when I did manifest, in the second chair at the table, the boy's chair, she did not even seem that startled. I wore a knitted cloche low on my forehead to cover the bullet hole and moved my chair in a way advantageous to the dim lighting of the room.

"How did you get in here?" she demanded, catching sight of me when she looked up from her journal. She clenched the pen in her hand like a javelin.

"Joan Vollmer, Patti. I was watching your reinterpretation of my death."

As could be expected, the revelation came as quite a jolt. She jumped up from her seat and bolted towards the door. "You old freak! You were spying on us! Get out now or I'll call the pigs!"

"Touch me Patti," I said following her as quickly as I could with my gimpy leg. She was frantically trying to undo all the locks on the door. "I can prove it to you if you touch me."

She wouldn't acknowledge my request, so to offer up irrefutable evidence of my nature, I walked through her, through the door, out into the hallway, then back into the room and beside her.

"I'm a ghost, Patti. An eidolon."

She frantically continued with the locks. As she was both tipsy and unnerved, all she could do was fumble them. "I'm asleep," she whispered, closing her eyes and shaking her head side to side. "I passed out in the chair, this is a dream…"

"You're awake," I interjected. "Robert left a little while ago. You've been drinking wine, writing in your journal."

An uncomfortable silence rested between us. A sort of stalemate. She could either resist believing what I was or she could accept it.

When she finally spoke it was with such a release of emotion I thought she might cry.

"Did I… *conjure* you?"

"I don't know exactly what you did, but it all lined up. I don't have long though. I'm like Cinderella at the ball. I can't dance all night. Can we sit down?"

She didn't respond but followed me back to the table, keeping as much of the small room between us as she could.

She stared at me for a good moment, then leaned across the table to touch me skittishly, like someone might if trying to gauge the heat of a hot stove. When her hand cut clear through the air, clear through *me*, she threw back her head and began reciting verses from Whitman: "And thee my soul, thy yearning amply fed at last, prepared to meet thy mates the eidolons!" She assailed her hands upon the tabletop and cried out, "Old Bull Lee's wife!" referring to my husband by his character's name in one of Jack's books. Talking a mile a minute and with much animation, she began speaking of her and the boy's reenactment of my death.

"It...it... was meant as a tribute, a *paean* to you and your relationship with Old Bull Lee... You are such an inspiration to me, Joan. You were the hippest, smartest girl on that scene, a real firecracker. Robert has said I'm so obsessed with my icons they're like my imaginary friends. I'll be writing in my journal and he'll say, 'What are you doing over there Patti Lee, communing with your dead pals?' I've always been thought of as a sort of 'little girl who cried wolf'... 'Oh Patti and her imagination!' they always say. That's probably why you came to me Joan, you knew from my mouth no one would believe it! A visit from you is just the sort of thing they would expect me to claim!"

She was so excitable and schizophrenic it dawned on me we might go on like this forever unless I got stern.

"Robert is homosexual Patti," I said. "His sexual encounters with men are not just some artistic experiment. I know all about the denials and justifications. I went through the same thing with Bill. I had as hard a time accepting it as you."

"Joan Vollmer Burroughs in my room at the Chelsea! Commiserating with me about man troubles!" She pulled her feet up into the seat of her chair and wrapped her arms around her legs, adjusting the skirt of her dress for modesty. "I've felt so jaded lately. My belief in the magic of the world has really been on the wane." She inhaled deeply and fidgeted with a loose gold band on her ring finger, twisting it in circles it as she spoke.

"At one time, Robert and I were like one person, Joan. *Psychic twins* I used to say. Telepathic, like you and Old Bull Lee. I'd always dreamed of meeting another artist to love and create with. Robert's my muse and my maker. I'm resistant to give that up no matter who he shares his bed with."

She must have forgotten I was untouchable because she started to reach across the table, then pulled back. "I feel so blessed to have this time with you, Joan."

"You're blessed to have someone to have this conversation with," I replied. "I had no one. At least no one who wasn't in some way caught up in our madness. You can't just talk to anyone about your lover, your husband, being fey. They don't understand why you just don't leave, that you can't just turn your feelings on and off like that. Then there's the denial. I used to say to Bill, 'How can you be a faggot when you fuck like a pimp?'"

A sly smile spread across her face that made me think she could relate.

"I need to ask you a favor, Patti. I want to know if my husband shot me on purpose. I want to know once and for all if my death really was just an accident."

"Oh Joan, I can assure you right now that it was! Lee was devastated by your death. It ruined him. It took him to depths so low, he had to write to find his way out. Your death is what inspired him to become a writer. It's the reason he writes now!"

"Bill had been writing for years before my death, Patti. He was starting to become more ambitious about it with encouragement from Allen and Jack. He was writing two books at the time of my shooting. I had read parts of them. One was about boys, the other was about junk."

"I'm staggered that you would even question it, Joan. Lee had no reason to do you in. You were the mother of his child. You had a partnership, a numinous understanding..."

"He'd been home for three days from a trip to South America with his boyfriend when I was shot. They were in South America for over two months, Patti. Two months! I don't know what happened over the course of that trip. Maybe the thought that once he came home— the looming threat of returning to *that* existence... I suspect he was done with us. Billy could go and live with his parents— and me, I don't think he really cared where I went, as long as it was away from him."

"Oh Joan, I don't believe that for a second. You had tolerated all of his lovers in the past. Whatever would have been his complaint?"

"I think he wanted to be free of the trappings and responsibility of a family, Patti. Free to be an artist, to bugger boys whenever he wanted to, with impunity. Free of my loud mouth, my ugly face. I moved my chair over here because the lighting is better and you won't get a good look at me. At my teeth. They're like rotting tombstones from all my years on Benzedrine. What you would see isn't damage done by any bullet. I was off the speed by then, but I was foul-mouthed lush with a gimpy leg from polio. Twenty-eight years old, but looking closer to fifty. I was only a few years older than you and you made me for an old freak when you first caught sight of me! And I can't be positive because I'd been drinking, but I think I saw something in Bill's eyes when he pointed the gun..."

"You were both drunk, Joan. That's probably why your recollection's so hazy. You were blitzed. You and Bill were at a party, at friend's house, when you were shot. You were performing your William Tell Act, something you'd done many times before..."

"No Patti. I remember what happened. I remember it clearly. Bill and I hadn't even come to the apartment I was shot at together. I hardly saw him over those three days after he returned from his trip. We met up at the apartment where I was shot by co-incidence. His lover, the boy he went to South America with, was one of five or so people who lived there. And I think it bothered Bill. He wanted me out of his life and there I was, a guest at his lover's apartment, and it made him feel like he'd never be free of me, he'd always have to tolerate my presence in some unbearable way or another. He'd come to the apartment to sell a gun. And I was at my wit's end with him, Patti. I had to call his parents for money to feed the children while he was off in South America gal-livanting with his catamite! We bantered there. I knew him so well, I knew just what to say to get him good and make it sting. He hated to be embarrassed. He was such a show-off, with a machismo streak a mile long. I made a comment, not even a clever one. I said, in front of his catamite, in front of his claque, I said, 'The big man with the gun who can't shoot straight.' You see, Bill was a great shot, it was one of the things he prided himself on, his marksmanship. I was being cheeky. I meant it as a double enten-dre. I just wanted a response. Some pathetic acknowledgement of my existence. And he said, 'Oh yeah?' And then to prove it, to prove me wrong, I let him put the glass on my head. It was the most interaction we'd had in months, Patti. Yes, it was something we'd done once before, but it wasn't any party trick. I wasn't suici-dal Patti. I would have *never* let him put that glass on my head if I thought for a second he might miss..."

"I don't believe it, Joan."

"I saw something in his eyes, Patti. I'm not saying it was a total set-up, but I think in that moment, he saw a way to get what he wanted...he saw a way out. What I'd like for you to do is, I'd like for you to put it out there for me. I'd like for you to say that you suspect I was murdered."

"Oh, Joan! I'm a fairly new face on the scene here. I don't want to alienate anyone. I'm a poet, Joan. I'm not any kind of investigative reporter..."

"You could write a poem. Nothing will happen to Bill, Patti. It was eighteen years ago. I don't want him rearrested. He already got his sentence, which he ran from, by the way. I just want some acknowledgement of what I think might have happened to me that night. Why doesn't anyone have the guts to say it aloud—to even question it? Is it because all of you who venerate him so would have to confront an ugliness about yourselves?"

"Look at my bookcase Joan! I'm a scholar of your lives!"

"What are you saying? Because you've read all of my husband's books you are somehow better *qualified* than I am to judge what happened to me that night?"

"William Burroughs is like another bible to me, Joan. He's one of the reasons I became an artist. He's one of the reasons I moved to New York..."

"Another *bible*...Do you like science fiction, Patti?"

"Science fiction? I mean, I suppose. I've read some Ray Bradbury..."

"What about gay pornography? Do you enjoy gay pornography, Patti?"

"I'm not against *any* kind of sexual expression, Joan. It's not what gets me off, if that's what you mean..."

"What about *pederasty*? *Child fucking*. How do you feel about child fucking, Patti? Because that's what my husband writes about. That's your *bible*. Or is the real reason my husband's your favorite writer what you think he *represents*? Gentleman-degeneracy with a

Harvard degree and a handsome hat? Is it the *kitsch* value of his lawlessness that you venerate? Is my husband your favorite writer because you're so frantic to viewed as *outsider* you'll pardon his transgressions so you can be associated with them?"

I was so angry now that I stood up and removed my cloche. "I'm sorry I came here tonight Patti, but I have no choice in who I come to. Because of that, if you keep with your crass reenactments, I may be back."

I picked up her pen from the table, the one she'd been using to write in her journal, and jammed it into the hole in my forehead. "Yours will wash away, Patti. Mine won't."

Then I left her there, at her table, in her room at that hollowed hotel.

Left her with the lepers.

***

Bill is dead now, so what does any of this matter?

I have not seen him since his passing, but I came across something the other day, something interesting. It was a transcript of an interview a man named George Laughhead did with my husband right before he died. I can't get into the logistics of how or where I saw it, but in it Mr. Laughhead concedes to something that I've always suspected.

He says, "I don't really care if William Burroughs murdered his wife."

My husband was *allowed* my death. His status as an icon allowed for him to transcend my shooting to such a degree it was no longer considered a criminal act, but a *celebrated* one.

In his old age, it appears Bill himself felt a little more emboldened to speak closer to the truth. In the same interview, he yells out, "SHOOT THE BITCH AND WRITE A BOOK....THAT'S WHAT I DID."

It has been said that the pen is mightier than the sword. And sometimes it is the sword.

Don't let me down.

Joan Vollmer Burroughs

The Satanic How-To Guide to Exalted Girldom

In *Double Trouble*, book one of Francine Pascal's seminal 1980's Young Adult series, *Sweet Valley High,* series protagonist Elizabeth Wakefield is slut-shamed by proxy.

Having-it-out with Elizabeth's twin sister, series antagonist Jessica Wakefield, over his father's plans to turn the Sweet Valley High football field into a public garden, Bruce Patman, the good-looking scion of one of the richest, most corrupt families in town says, "Hey, when it comes to having a disgrace in the family, just consider your sister, Elizabeth, the *pub-crawler.*"

Pub-crawler = bar-slut.

But Patman's slut-shaming of Elizabeth is based on erroneous information, and a case of mistaken identity. Studious, blonde-haired, blue-eyed, Aryan-idealized Elizabeth would never go to a *bar*. It was Jessica, Elizabeth's doppelganger down to the pea-sized dimple in her left cheek, who was groped and degraded at Kelly's Roadhouse Saloon, after being absconded there by the tattooed, Camaro-driving Rick Andover; he of the "ice cool handsomeness of Clint Eastwood, and a hint of dangerousness lurking in his dark sultry eyes."

When the police are called to intervene— taking the sleazy Rick away in handcuffs— the notoriously machinating Jessica gives them Elizabeth's name instead of her own.

Rumors fly, first-world problems ensue.

I hadn't read *Double Trouble* or any of the 150+ other titles in the *Sweet Valley High* series in close to twenty-five years. When *Double Trouble* was first published in 1983, I was seven years old. I had a weakness for books in a series format, and before *Sweet Valley*, my favorite books were *The Little House* series by Laura Ingalls Wilder. The two series couldn't have been more different—though they had one major similarity. Both series focused heavily on the relationship between sisters.

My own sister was two years older than me. We shared the same room, where she would take out my journal from under my mattress, and correct the spelling errors. She also introduced me to the *Sweet Valley High* books. (In what would become a major motif of our relationship as young girls, my sister would start out with an interest, then I would run with that interest, and take it over.) I kept track of the estimated release dates of new titles, and would run down to our local bookstore, dizzy with anticipation. Sometimes I would pay for the new book with a Ziploc baggie full of change. I was a total crackhead for these books.

I had an incredible amount of gumption as a young girl, while my sister was much more reticent. I remember her saying two words to me constantly: "Stop spazzing." I craved drama, and was way too susceptible to what I read in *Sweet Valley High*, eating up every superficial morsel and internalizing what those details said about me, and my value as a young girl. It was as if I took the attitudes and ideals espoused in the books as marching orders. The *Sweet Valley High* series was like my *Satanic How-To Guide to Exalted Girldom.*

Some of what I took from the books was in conflict with the reality of my Middle School existence. For example, in the books, beautiful, popular Jessica is the captain of the Sweet Valley High cheerleading team, but at my school, the sport teams were nothing to rah-rah-rah about, and the cheerleading squad didn't resemble anything close to the Battalion of Babes described in the series. Still, being a cheerleader was clearly on the checklist to exalted-ness— so I tried out, but didn't make the team. Undeterred, I discovered that our local Park and Rec had an all-volunteer squad, and got my hands on a pair of pom-poms.

Because pretty, popular girls were almost always depicted as being wealthy or upper middle-class, I began to lie about my family's finances. Undermining my fib was our modest, slightly-run down home next to a gas station on a major thoroughfare in town, where my sister and I could be seen in the front yard, doing gymnastics. Thinking on my feet, I incorporated the gas station into my lie. My family owned it, I said. We were reluctantly slumming in the house next door so my parents could keep a closer eye on their business.

There were other girls like me who had obviously internalized the same kind of socio-economic insecurity. One day, I had a fight with a friend who came from a family of even lesser financial means than my own. The insult that we lobbed back and forth at each other like a hot piece of coal was whose family was poorer, hers or mine.

Her: "Your family's poorer!"

Me: "Yours is!"

Her: "Yours is!"

Then she claimed it was actually *her* family that owned the gas station next door to my house.

But the crowning mark of ultimate exalted girldom was having your looks deemed powerful and persuasive enough to move product (or as it was phrased in Barbizon ad that ran in the back of YM magazine at the time): *To be a model, or just look like one.* Though Jessica and Elizabeth weren't models *per se*, it was intimated in the books that modeling was an option that always remained open to them. Maybe it was an option that was also open to me? I was optimistic, as I was still young enough where I had yet to be told that I was "ugly" by anyone. (It would come very, very soon.) Until I could find out for sure, I figured if I picked some fringe magazine, and said I had a spread in it, no one would be able to investigate. The cooking magazine *Bon Appetit* fit the bill.

All these years later, I have an artifact from this time period that illustrates just how important all this superficiality was to me.

In the summer of 1987, when I was eleven years old, my best friend came back from camp with incredible stories about her experience there: the dances, the romances, the fireside feuds. It sounded like one big soap opera of canoes and canoodling. It sounded like a *Sweet Valley High* book with an Outward Bound backdrop. A lot of her stories revolved around a camp stud named Geoff Scott, a twelve-year-old soccer player who lived a few towns away from us. He was the boy all the girls at camp had pined for, and all the boys wanted on their team when playing Capture the Flag. My friend had his address in her camp yearbook, so I decided to write him a letter.

It's hard for me to read my letter to Geoff now, because I know there were many more just like it, and the one I still have was most likely a rough draft of a letter I actually sent. In the letter, I list all the cars my parents supposedly own, along with the lesser models they supposedly traded-in that year to get the newer ones. My letter to Geoff is like a *MASH* game, but one in which I decide that I can have it all: the mansion, the apartment and the house, so why deny myself anything? My lies are also a time capsule of my interests at the time: at eleven, I'm still playing with toys, because I say my father owns a toy shop. I'm still enamored of horses, because I say I own a horse (named Daisy, my favorite flower) too. And there it is, casually dropped in towards the end of my letter, in case Geoff has yet to be convinced of my virtue by way of my vast material riches: I'm a model— and an exhausted one, from some local assignment; I ask him to forgive my letter's spelling errors. I couldn't just leave the letter lying around, where my sister might have corrected it for me, that would have revealed to her the extent of my lies. While my head was floating in the clouds of superficial fantasy, my sister was devouring a book about a troubled young woman who'd sought refuge in drugs, and the burgeoning 1970's punk scene: Deborah Spungen's memoir about her daughter Nancy Spungen, *And I Don't Want to Live This Life*.

Reinforcing that a little lying could do a lot of good, Geoff wrote back immediately. We talked on the phone, covering so much ground in so little time, that we agreed on the names of our future children, which I drew on the petals of a flower and hung on my bedroom wall (Renee, Gloria, Stacey, and Ryan, I was also a big *Kids Incorporated* fan). I don't remember being nervous about meeting Geoff, which he wanted to do ASAP—only excited. By today's standards, I was an epistolary Catfish, but I didn't hesitate to meet him at all. I may have written a bunch of lies in my letters, but I don't remember feeling like I had anything to hide. It never occurred to me to fake a modeling portfolio, or steal a horse. I think I thought by making these brash claims about myself, and my family, that I could use them to grab a person's attention, then from there, I hoped, the real me would be good enough to hold it.

I remember exactly what I wore the day that Geoff and I met. It was also the outfit I planned to wear on the first day of 6th grade, which meant it was an ensemble that I gave high marks: a red acid-washed skirt, and red and white short sleeved shirt that cropped at my waist. My hair at the time was very short, as evidenced by my school photo, which would be taken a few weeks later. We had made plans to meet at the shopping center downtown, and I was so excited that I got there over an hour early, and spent the extra time walking in circles, fussing with my hair in the reflection of store windows.

His mother's Mercedes pulled up to the curb, and he stepped out.

He was wearing a pink polo shirt, khaki shorts and boat shoes. He was extremely preppy and had thick, wavy Ken doll hair. I don't remember thinking for a moment that in meeting me, he might be let down. If he was, he was a good sport about it, though it may have been that he felt like a hostage, as he was dependent on his mother's return a few hours later to make his getaway. We walked over to Dunkin Donuts, and I was not shy in the least, grabbing his hand and announcing that because "Walk Like an Egyptian" was playing on the radio, it was now our song. I had made plans to bring him by the house of one of the more popular girls in my class who lived close to downtown; she came outside and performed perfect gymnastics for us on the lawn. We were her spectators, and as Geoff sat next to me, watching her, for the first time that afternoon, a sliver of doubt entered my head: I wondered if he wished I was her.

Before he left, I think Geoff kissed me on the cheek, I'm not positive as I may have invented this detail later for the benefit of the popular girl. If he did, our first kiss was also our last kiss, because a few days later, he broke up with me, over the phone. The reason he gave me was that he'd reconnected with an "old girl-friend."

Strangely, considering I'd named imaginary babies with him, I don't remember being all that devastated, (a testament to the resilience of my *jeune coeur*), but I was definitely hurt, and needed some kind of dramatic distraction to hold me over until school started. I snuck over to my sister's side of the room, and decided to examine her new book, *And I Don't Want to Live This Life*. There was a blonde on the cover, but her look was 180 degrees different from that of the wholesome, sun-kissed Jessica and Elizabeth. She didn't even look like a natural blonde, and with her purple-painted lips and pistol necklace, she looked mean. She was Nancy Spungen, and once I started reading her mother's memoir about her life and murder, I couldn't put it down.

Thanks to the book, I discovered a whole new world to be intrigued by—and a poster boy to pine for, with his own "hint of dangerousness lurking in his dark sultry eyes." Except my new poster boy's eyes had been closed eternally, as he'd been dead for almost ten years.

It didn't matter. Sid Vicious would save my soul from *Sweet Valley High*.

A Totally Gruesome Document Detailing a Relationship

Journal entries Oct.-Dec. 2012

I feel like we've lost a lot of steam in this relationship.

I don't want to be a novelty item.

The other night, while we were talking about union organizing with our opposing viewpoints, I was searching, stammering, for the right word, and you gave me this look: it was like there was steam coming out of your eyeballs. You looked like you hated me. Like you wanted me to *die*, because I support unions.

We are boredom associates.

A relationship should make you feel better about yourself.

You said there was a risk to having sex like we do, that it becomes fucking, not intimacy. Totally loveless. Parts, not people.

The first kiss is when you drop me off and say goodnight.

~

We were having anal sex and it hurt.

I don't mind anal sex when it's done right, I usually enjoy it, but it's not something I crave with any daily regularity, so I was resentful and annoyed that you went there, after we had just done it that way the night before. Anal sex had become part of our rut, and I was quietly simmering, angry that you didn't seem to care about our rut.

I, on the other hand, had addressed our rut in an offhand manner.

Our sex life had been incredible, but now it was formulaic. Why? How can passion be lost so quickly? Where does it go?

You stopped kissing me.

Here is our sexual routine:

Take your clothes off.

I put my clothes on the loveseat that you had moved upstairs in better times; times befitting the transformation of your bedroom into a lover's boudoir: antique mirrors, four-poster California king-sized bed, two reupholstered foot stools, and my own set of white mahogany dresser drawers, filled with my neatly folded bed shirts (your cast off button-downs, which you put away, ironed and starched, shoulders-squared, military-style), and lingerie I brought from home. We'd been together only two weeks when you bought me a toothbrush and put it the bathroom. The gesture made me nervous, something so small, yet so rife with expectation, and not a cheap toothbrush. You told me you loved me two weeks into our relationship, while we were having sex. I felt embarrassed for you. I told you it was ok, I understood, you'd gotten caught up in the moment, though you never took it back. Sixty-year-old man as stereotyped teenage girl. It was a very human moment.

Take your clothes off.

Which also means my pretty bra and underwear, which I would like to showcase, but you couldn't care less about. I used to attribute this to the fact that you'd been a hippie, the real deal, a relic from the winds of San Francisco hitting the East Coast in the sixties. You don't undress me. It is understood that I undress myself, though you know I would prefer it if you did.

Bend over, spread your legs, I want access.

Earlier in our relationship, you had asked me my favorite sexual position and I said from behind. I thought you were gung-ho on doing it this way because of my answer. I was wrong. It turned out to be a serendipitous response.

Wait: before entry, you need to get hard.

I drop to my knees and suck you off. Sometimes it takes work to get you hard. You take Cialis, which I imagine is totally normal for someone your age.

The first time we had sex, you had a hard time getting it up and said, "I'm so embarrassed, this has never happened before." I remember thinking, "Almost a year without sex, and here I am, splayed and naked, foiled by the devil impotence!" The dress I'd been wearing earlier that night, I'd gotten online, second-hand, from a pin-up hula-hoop Satanist. You, who had no prior experience with impotence, went downstairs and got your cock ring. I hope I don't sound mean, I don't want to be. I hope I don't sound bitter, I'm not. It must be an incredibly embarrassing thing for a man to address, especially so early in a relationship.

So, if you're hard from my sucking and your talking and directing: you're always talking and directing. Once intimacy left the relationship, talking and directing took over, or maybe your want for talking and directing pushed it out. No more spontaneity, no more creativity, and we had been so creative, and spontaneous. It's funny; I never knew I cared so much about intimacy. I suppose I've always been lucky in having it.

Is that cock hard enough for you, baby? Suck my nipple. I want you open. Easy access.

Uh-hum, uh-hum. I contributed to the rut. I thought I enjoyed submissiveness. I didn't know it would become my only role.

This was the problem when the anal sex hurt.

Earlier, you'd asked me to bite your cock. *Chew on it*, you said. I guess I chewed with a gusto, because you told me that I was hurting you, so I stopped. When you tried to jam your cock up my ass for the second time in as many nights, I was already stewing with resentment. It was part of what I meant when I told you to stop. I couldn't take it anymore. It was like you were fucking me like that so you wouldn't have to look at me. My saying *stop* was a deviation from the script. The leitmotif of our sex life has become I take what you give me. I follow your direction and honor your script. You're allowed to say stop because it hurts, but I'm not.

Early in our relationship, during the honeymoon period in which you presented yourself as a warm, funny, loving, text all the time, think I'm the smartest, most beautiful, best piece of ass you've ever had all the time person, something similar happened. We were having sex, and you accidentally jabbed me in the ass, full force. Searing fucking pain. If the job of comedy is to help us come to terms with tragedy, I felt that I understood the entire trope of prison jokes completely. This was while our relationship was still in its infancy, when it still had passion and intimacy, and you'd stopped immediately, because that is what you do when you hurt someone, even someone you care about only a little bit. You stop.

Last night, I told you that you hurt me, and we broke up.

It's funny when things come full circle, and you can tie it all up in a neat little bow.

~

One thing that might be hard for me to think about, that might trigger nostalgia in me for our relationship, is your glasses. I've always had a thing for Indiana Jones, ever since I was a little girl, and you always reminded me of Indiana Jones, erudite Professor Jones in his university classroom, with your glasses on.

You said poor impulse control could cause you problems. You said if the permission was there, you might take advantage of it, and told me an anecdote about rough sex where you threw your ex-girlfriend across the room. You said there were no hard feelings, but it was a revelation to you, that you needed to watch yourself.

When did you first decide I wasn't the person you idealized? (There's a part of me that wants to live up to all expectations, even the unrealistic ones.) The night I took too much Xanax and got sloppy? When I stammered in the union conversation? I felt you getting resentful toward me. Still, you wanted to see me and fuck me and be with me all the time. Maybe it's your depression and uncertainty about your future. Maybe it's our twenty-five-year age difference. What hurts the most is the rejection. Underneath it all, my worst fear is, like everyone else's, that I am unlovable. My second worst fear is that I am like everyone else.

The loss, a month ago, of the compliments, the affectionate texts, the kissing. When I mentioned it last night, you wouldn't address it.

"How come I felt closer to you at the beginning of our relationship?"

"I have no answer for that." Pause. "What do you suggest we might do?"

"I don't know. I can't be in a relationship with a person who doesn't want to kiss me."

No response.

When the kissing stopped, at first I assumed it was some domination game. Did you want me to beg you? Did you want to see if I'd put up with it?

I had mentioned it once before and you'd acted like you'd just "forgotten" and went out of your way to kiss me for the rest of the night, then the next day, back to no kissing, and now you knew what you were doing, and how it made me feel.

"Don't do anything rash," you said to me on the drive home last night. Then, "I'm going to be sad, but I'm not going to beat myself up over this."

Suck and Fuck had become a mantra. For some reason, you decided that I loved to hear you say it and would ask me to repeat it back to you. Strangely, five years ago, right around this time, Henry and I had broken up (you told me you didn't want to hear anything else about Henry after you accidentally read a short story I'd written about him. "I don't want to know any more than I need to about your weirdo ex-boyfriends," you said) and he was driving me home after what I'd stumbled across on his computer: *Suck and Fuck*. It was the subject line of one of the emails in his inbox. He'd been messaging transsexual prostitutes on Craigslist, looking to hook up with them. *I like to suck and fuck*, he'd written, as a way of introducing himself.

The full circle of things that don't work out.

It's worth noting that when I started crying at your kitchen table, I heard you rounding the corner, and thought for certain you were coming to console me. Instead, you just walked on by. I can hear the Dionne Warwick song in my head as I write this.

Earlier in the night, you'd said something, offhandedly, about a friend who was dating someone, who in your opinion (but not hers) was beneath her. You said something about "any port in a storm."

Is that what I am to you? Is that why you're with me, despite your coldness? Am I *any port in a storm*?

I'll never date an older man again. As pathetic as it sounds, it pains me that I do not have the power of Anna Nicole Smith.

~

The pain I feel is not of heartbreak, but of rejection and scam. So many things about you are repulsive to me now, but they were always repulsive. The hairdresser who started to cry after you berated her for making you wait for your appointment. The constant reminder of the cost of your Nordstrom shirts. ($80.) How many times in different company did I listen to you tell the personal shopper story? There could be sweetness, but it fell away. I tried to always be sweet.

If you were to call now, I'd be disassociated from my feelings. My anger would be dissipated; no, I'd just be disconnected from it. The time to stay away from the phone is now. I have Xanax brain. It wouldn't be that my feelings had changed, they'd just be misplaced.

I could be so many things if the little nagging, treacherous voice inside my head would just STFU.

"Tragic hoes."

I thought I wanted to be degraded, but I wanted to be degraded with love.

You wanted me to talk during sex and what came out was, "You hate me."

~

It's not my birthright, my job, to school old men. I'm not the revelation that comes along in their twilight years to melt their cold, cold hearts. My vagina is not a last chance saloon.

I said once that my advice to you would be to have sex with a "fat" woman and love a child. I said it like I was joking, but I'm proud of myself for having said it, because the sentiment is true. I could tell that it resonated with you, because you were speechless, and you're never speechless. Courtney Love said in an interview once that after she and Kurt got married, she encouraged him to have sex with a model, because she wanted him to enjoy the cliché rock star spoils of success, because they had both (but Kurt especially) come from a community that had made its identity on rejecting all of that, disavowing the whole rock star thing. What she was saying was that she wanted him to feel free. That was what I meant when I said that to you. That you need to do something, experience something, free of any phony pretenses. Just you and the other person, not you, the other person, and the politics of what it means to be a man. At your age, you might not have that much time left.

~

I don't understand. When I was young, it seemed like men (boys?) used to fall in love with me all the time. Girls (women?) wanted to be my friend. I was smart and witty. What happened? I lost my imagination. My belief in magic. I got frayed.

After Henry and I broke up, after I found the Craigslist emails on his computer, in a moment of weakness, I texted him:

It kills me that you can resist me, I wrote.

He texted back: *I can't.*

But he could.

He had also gone inexplicably cold.

~

Henry used to say all his ex-girlfriends were crazy. You say all your ex-girlfriends were alcoholics.

Beware of any man who puts all his ex-girlfriends in the same ghetto.

~

I want a man who will chase after me. You tripped over my baggage, when it could have been easily navigated by more agile feet.

A definitive mark of maturity is the last time you told someone to eat shit and die.

The problem with this relationship is that look on your face.

ROUND 2

He said nothing, just sat there impatiently like he was deigning, stooping, limboing low to spend time with me, a drama queen. He kept reiterating it was a spontaneous act to come see me. He said it so many times it was obvious it was anything but. He's not as smart as he pretends to be.

I think I'm becoming repulsive.

The TV was on in the other room, and I heard a character on a sitcom say, "any port in a storm." The writing on the wall is a warning. But why do I still want to see him? Why didn't I just ask him to leave? Why do I tell myself it's only to make sure it's over? It's drugs. I'm trying to recapture the high of him.

I have a strong desire to take a shower in the dark.

No country for old men except my vagina.

~

I went to Planned Parenthood this morning, convinced my IUD was coming out, and afraid to go anywhere near the hard black plastic thing emerging from my vagina. I was afraid of my own organ, Germaine Greer would not have been proud. It was his cock ring (a small, tight elastic, not the spiky, dinosaur-looking things that my punk rock friends used to have). I told the doctor, *thank you for everything, you are beautiful, but I will never be coming back, I will be switching OBGYN's immediately, out of shame.* She said *don't be embarrassed, young lady, I've found all sorts of ephemeral objects in vaginas–shampoo bottle caps, erasers.* She thought the cock ring was part of a condom, and I did not correct her. I'm not going to bother telling him. He'd probably be pissed I didn't retrieve it from the hazardous waste receptacle.

On my walk home from Planned Parenthood, I thought of my old friend Pete who tried to claim that he was the first writer to ever describe a vagina as being like a "velvet purse." (That description can be found in literature going back to, like, the 17th century.) Then I thought about Cameron, my boyfriend when I was thirteen, who said that he and his sister had written a song called "Otters in the Stream," which turned out to be the Kenny Rogers/

Dolly Parton duet "Islands in the Stream," with the words changed a little. I'd believed Cameron, too, 'til I heard the original song playing in the frozen food aisle at the supermarket.

~

What's important is revealed under dire circumstances, otherwise it's confused.

The girl was sad. She felt beaten down. She felt she had tried and was a good catch. Yes, she had her baggage, but she was redeemable, like a plastic bottle at the bottle return. She was a good project, with a reward on the other side. Loyal, attractive, loving, fun in the sack.

If you are sixty, on your own, not a widower, not gay, nor recently divorced, chances are you might be insufferable.

I asked the million dollar question, and got the five-cent answer.

In a traumatic situation, you focus on the object—the gun, the knife—not the person behind it.

~

ARGOSIES: an abundant supply.

The night my dad died had been a shitty day, an abject lesson in no matter how bad things are, they can always get much, much worse. It was the night of my high school's Christmas Ball, which was like a winter prom, but open to the whole school. My junior year, my girlfriends and I had started importing our love interests from New Haven, the freakier-looking, the better, and this was in the '90s, when letting your freak flag fly still took dedication and ingenuity. Kids today have it so freak-easy, and as a side result, children no longer point and whisper, and old women don't clutch their pocketbooks. My date was a sinister boy named Andrew, who looked like a living, breathing corpse, and wore his hair in a million skinny red braids, which sounds horrible now, but at the time, I found to be alluring. He'd come in on the train from New Haven, and came to school with me the day of the dance. You used to be able to do that at my school, bring your friends with you, if their parents wrote a note giving permission. After lunch, someone pulled the fire alarm, and Andrew was taken from the class he'd been in with me. The whole thing was an opportunistic set-up: when Andrew and I had gone into the principal's office that morning to drop off his note, it was obvious that the way he looked put the principal on edge. He had nothing to do with the fire alarm. Andrew was handcuffed and taken to the train station in a cop car. The police stayed and waited at the station until the train physically left to make sure that he was gone. I remember hysterically throwing myself onto the floor of the girl's bathroom, and writing *FTW* on my backpack in red magic marker. Of course, I still went to the dance. My friends and I had put so much effort into our crazy outfits, and they still had their freaky dates to go with. When I got home that night, my mother was standing in the kitchen, crying. My father was dead.

For a young boy, dead dads destroy dreams. For a young girl, they shape future lovers.

~

He thinks about salvaging our relationship in taglines, slogans, like you see on movie posters and DVD covers. Movie man/action hero speak. *What would you be willing to do to save the best fuck of your life?* Sometimes when he's thinking these thoughts, he thinks he hears the faint toot-toot of a Klondike whistle: *Save the cunt, save the world!*

Greatest quotes:

After seeing a picture of me from high school: "It's probably good you weren't attractive when you were younger. If you were attractive then, you might not be attractive now. You might have used it all up." (This is an example of male beauty math.)

"Today you're the best-looking girl in the room, but this won't always be the case."

"I wasn't attracted to you because of your beauty. Oh no...."

~

A young girl is crouching by a bridge. Below, a man and woman find sexual congress in the dirt. The young girl has never seen such a thing. She's not naive, she's read books. The man's ass rises, then descends. The woman's hands dig into the muscles of his ass. The young girl is so lost in the scene, she can't look away.

Tell me what you like the most.

What it is that gives you hope.

What leads you to lock your legs and get out of bed in the morning?

~

I know why I am attracted to older men. I like the banter. It's the way I used to talk to my dad, to my grandfather. I sit down on their couch, put the dirty soles of my shoes all over their clean table, and they play cards, and I say dumb, silly things, and try to be shocking. I've found a way to stay a kid forever. Or at least a little while longer. So I sleep with it.

~

This morning on my walk to work, I made my regular morning stop at a local convenience store to get coffee and cigarettes. When I got to the counter, there was a problem with the credit card machine, so I had to look in my wallet for money, which I hardly ever carry with me, as I used my debit card for everything. The change I had in my wallet was down to the dregs, so I put back the cigarettes, but felt obligated to pay for the coffee, as I'd made it according to my preferences. I dug around in my wallet and managed to come up with the $1.40, but I felt on the spot with other customers in line behind me, so I tried to be fast. I caught a flash of my lucky quarter in my wallet: My lucky quarter is a quarter that's a quarter of a quarter; I'm not sure how it got that way, or where I got it, but it's been my good luck charm for years. I gave the cashier my change and beat it. When I got down the street, the thought went through my mind: I didn't just give her my lucky quarter, did I? I knew that if I looked, and found the quarter gone, I'd make myself turn around and go back to the store, and as a result, be late for work, so I made myself wait until I got to work to look in my bag. Of course, once I got there, I couldn't find it, and started to panic. That afternoon, I had my annual evaluation with my boss. I had three poems under consideration at *Highfalutin* magazine. Without my lucky quarter, my world might fall apart. Maybe everything good in my life that had happened over the last few years had happened on account of that lucky quarter. I did not want to find out.

I called my mother, my Roman Oracle of Delphi for everything.

"Mom," I said. "I think I may have paid with my lucky quarter at Henny Penny. Should I call and ask the counter person to look in the cash register?"

She said, "Don't fret Chicken Little, the sky is not falling. Yet."

No, she didn't say that. She said that she had been in the same store that morning, coincidentally, and if it was still the same woman working behind the counter, she seemed nice. I reassured myself by imagining that customers would bristle at the sight of my quarter if she were to attempt to give it to them as change.

"Hello," I said, after looking up the phone number to Henny Penny on my phone, "I was just in there and think I may have paid for my coffee with my lucky quarter. Could you please look for me? I hate to be a pain in the ass."

She was nice, as my Oracle had predicted.

"I'm sorry," she said, with sympathy that sounded legit.

"Could you look for me, if you get the chance, and if you find it, put it aside?"

"Of course," she said, "but it sounds very distinctive, and I'm looking in the cash register right now, and I don't see it."

"Could I leave you my name and phone number in case it turns up?"

"Of course," she said. She liked that affirmation. "I have a pen right here."

The idea that my cosmic protection shield might be gone forever left me feeling incredibly exposed. Having a good luck charm is a lot like having a child, but a child that's also a parent. You can't imagine your life without it. You have to take care of your good luck charm as much as it takes good care of you.

My co-workers were starting to arrive and I felt weird frantically searching my bag in front of them, so I went into the bathroom and pulled down the diaper changing table in the handicap stall. The thing about belief in magic is that it actually creates magic. I was tongue-tied already, just saying "good morning" to my co-workers. I was starting to think it might be a good idea to just feign sickness and go home.

But then I found it, sliver of silver, quarter of a quarter, it had fallen out of my wallet and hidden itself behind a discarded gum wrapper in my bag. I chew a lot of gum, and no one could ever accuse me of being a litter bug.

My day could start anew, so many Armageddons averted.

I told myself I would find a new therapist soon.

~

I told him about the cock ring. I got shit-faced and found the humiliation of the situation to be too much not to share. We were getting along very well last night, which is another reason. I felt a measure of familiarity and comfort. I asked him to spit on/strangle me. It was fun, but we're both too complicated for loving. Things no longer seem that dire or desperate now that I've accepted this. As we were leaving his house, the garbage man asked us if I was his daughter. He didn't answer, and turned away with a grumpy look on his face. I don't think he saw me turn toward the man and nod my head yes.

They All Want to Piss on You

High on heroin, we had sex on his mom's blue-grey dining room carpet, and the small of my back was ripped raw and bloody by the carpet's stiff fibers. Curly-q's of frayed skin formed a frame around a tramp stamp of a wet wound. He went into the kitchen to get paper towels to clean me, and me from the carpet.

"Why didn't you say anything?" he asked.

"It was strange," I answered. "It didn't really hurt, but I knew that if we didn't stop, there would be a consequence. I had to make a choice. Usually the pain makes the decision for you. I decided not to decide."

I watched in the dining room mirror as he dabbed the area of my back with hydrogen peroxide and care.

"This might leave a scar," he said. "I'm not going to lie. I kind of like the idea that I may have scarred you forever." His eyes gave off an electrical medicated sparkle.

Over the next few weeks, he'd randomly lift the back of my shirt to chart the healing process.

When we last saw each other, the scab had fallen off, revealing a faded blue-grey bruise underneath, a surprisingly close match to the color of his mother's carpet.

There was a slight scar, but years later, only I, knowing what to look for, could ever make it out.

***

A few weeks into our coupling, my present boyfriend and I were having sex on the industrial carpet in his work shop. We'd been drinking, and were still in that early stage of a relationship, when you are polite and considerate, and on your best behavior. He was grinding into me, the small of my back flush with the carpet's rough surface. I could feel it this time— the scraping by what felt like wire-brush bristles, back and forth, up and down— the carpet as sandpaper, my back as a piece of wood. My boyfriend had read something I'd written online and decided I was a masochist. So early in our relationship, I didn't want to let him down.

When we finished, I stood up.

"Oh my goodness," he said. "You're bleeding."

He went to go retrieve his first aid kit. He's like that. Every situation has its dovetailing tool. He came back, his hands fishing around inside the plastic box, looking, I assumed, for some kind of bandage.

"The spot is too awkward," I said. "I don't think anything would stay on."

He touched his finger softly to the wound. "Your beautiful back. I think I might have scarred you..."

For a moment he seemed genuinely mournful.

"I kind of like the idea I may have scarred you forever."

***

One more.

A few years ago, I became painfully thin. The only thing I didn't like about my size was my breasts. Every part of me had been reduced, my breasts included, and I became intrigued with the idea of getting a breast job.

I was seeing a guy in Brooklyn, who made a good salary.

"You should pay for me to get a breast job," I suggested, one Saturday morning, over coffee.

He seemed to think about it.

"What if we broke up?" he said. "I wouldn't want another guy touching the breasts I paid for. Nah, I don't think I like that."

"Obviously, you must have some doubts about of our relationship, if when you look into the future, you see some other man touching my breasts."

"I don't like it. Maybe I'd do it if we were married."

"Well, I wouldn't want to be married to a person who didn't trust me enough to pay for my breast job unless we were married."

That seemed to put him for a loop. His large salary wasn't based on intellect.

"I'd have to think about it," he said, a sneaky grin spreading across his face. "I do kind of like the idea of scarring you forever."

Herbert Huncke Herbert Huncke Herbert Huncke

Copping is a muscle, and muscles have memory.

In the summer of 1994, I had just graduated from high school, and was homeless. My mother had kicked me out of the house, and would only let me come home if I agreed to her one condition: I had to go to, and complete rehab. I'd attempted rehab once before, and found it unbearable; I'd schemed to get myself kicked out. There was just too much going on in the world outside that I didn't want to miss, and I hadn't been doing heroin long enough to equate it with any real kind of misery. I was on my own for the first time in my life, and had no qualms about sleeping outside, if it came down to it. My mother's one condition was a weak extortion.

My best friend Chelsea had just been released from the fabled Silver Hill Hospital, where her parents had sent her after she overdosed on heroin in a McDonald's bathroom stall. Edie Sedgwick had been to Silver Hill, and it had a hairdressing salon. I was jealous. Maybe I would have been able to endure my own intended 28 day stay if I'd been sent to a rehab that cush. One of the patients at Silver Hill with Chelsea was a good-looking young man with a head of thick, dark hair who kept love letters from Courtney Love in a box in his room. He'd regale Chelsea with all sorts of wild stories about Courtney, who'd just lost her husband, Kurt Cobain, to suicide a few months before. Kurt and I had been in different rehabs at the same time; I felt a quiet kinship with him as we'd both left the treatment centers we'd been forced into against our will.

Chelsea's roommate at Silver Hill was an attractive young woman named Alex. Alex's father had gotten rich selling high-waisted jeans to lower-income women across America. She'd been sent to Silver Hill by her parents for an eating disorder. Growing up on the peripherals of the fashion industry, Alex had been a model, and was bulimic. Silver Hill was a dual diagnosis program, which meant they treated emotional problems as well as drug and alcohol ones, and Chelsea was also being treated for cutting herself while she was there. She and Alex had come up with an agreement to support each other while in treatment: Chelsea wouldn't cut, if Alex didn't throw up. But the reverse was also true, and possibly the more effective motivator: Chelsea would cut, if Alex vomited. They had managed to keep this agreement a secret from the staff.

Alex was discharged from Silver Hill first, and a week after Chelsea's release, a Lincoln town car came to pick her up to squire her to Alex's family's Upper East Side townhouse. The town car stopped behind the supermarket where I'd been sleeping, and picked me up too.

It was a warm summer day and we were both so excited. Alex had an itinerary planned for us while we were in the city. We would have free reign of the Lincoln town car. Chelsea had told Alex I'd spent the summer homeless, and Alex had offered to take me shopping. I met Alex quickly; she was pale and statuesque, with bright blonde hair, and wore round Jackie O style sunglasses as she fluttered about the townhouse, getting dressed. I hadn't been so excited for what lay ahead since I was a kid, and my family would go on budget vacations to Cape Cod. Alex had an appointment with her therapist and asked the housekeeper to make us whatever we wanted to eat, and gave Chelsea two hundred dollars. The money was for incidentals, and for heroin, a drug Chelsea had told Alex all about, and Alex wanted to try.

We didn't know anyone in New York City to cop from, so we had the driver drop us off on St. Marks Place, and asked him to wait. We hit the streets, eyeing everyone we passed. We were walking towards Tompkins Square Park, a destination for homeless young people with punk rock sensibilities where I'd copped other times when I'd been in the city.

There is a waxy, sort of preserved Madame Tussaud's look to heroin users. In the same way that crackheads have sharp, spastic mannerisms, people on heroin have their own identifying characteristics: they look like they are intoxicated by sleep; they radiate a sort of toxic languor.

Two men passed us. They looked like they'd stepped out of a street scene in *Midnight Cowboy*; they looked like the sort of people I envisioned whenever I read anything about the old automat Horn and Hardart in Times Square. One of the men wore a child-size leather jacket, his arms poking out at the elbows. The other was hunchbacked and walked with a cane. All I could think was *Herbert Huncke Herbert Huncke Herbert Huncke*. We approached them, our want stronger than our shame.

"Um..." I'd learned that the best way to present myself when asking a stranger for anything illicit was with self-effacement. "Do you think you could you help me and my friend...?"

I left it to hang in the air. If I was right, they would just need me to clarify which, coke or dope, and how much.

They looked at each other.

"You aren't cops?"

Our appearances were testimonials. Chelsea had short bleached blonde hair with skinhead girl sideburns and fringe bangs, and the stubble on my shaved head was dyed black. Some cops will go to the trouble—my friend George was once busted smoking a joint by a cop with a Mohawk—but most, I assume, aren't paid enough and are too vain.

"No."

"You'll buy for us too?"

"Yes."

"We're going to have to take a walk. How much do you want?"

"A bundle, plus the two for you. Twelve?"

"We need to go to the Bowery."

Up close, the man with the cane was much younger than he had first appeared to be, due to his curled body. We talked as we walked, Chelsea, friendly and curious about everything, blabbed away, talking about rehab, what we were doing in the city, our car and driver. I was quieter, because copping always made me extremely anxious. Not so much about the police, though that anxiety definitely played a part, but because I couldn't relax until I had it. The outcome in ellipsis until I had the dope in my body did something to my bowels. I walked along like a duck, because I had to shit.

As we approached a side street off the Bowery, the man in the leather jacket asked for the money. His friend with the cane stayed with us, and my sphincter relaxed a bit. He made no moves to hobble off, a good indication that they had no plans to rip us off.

The man in the leather jacket returned a few minutes later, sidled up beside me, and slipped me the dope.

"Come over with me. I'll introduce you," he said.

This was an incredibly generous gesture; most middle men prefer to stay in the middle, as it's such a profitable spot.

"Ok."

I turned the corner, and followed him to a store front with the grating pulled down. Outside, on a plastic chair that looked like it had been stolen from an elementary school, sat a short, fat Asian man, with a wet towel draped around the back of his neck, and a red dragon tattooed on the top of his head. He resembled a sort of biker Buddha.

"Sammy, this is my friend."

The man's eyes were closed, but he quickly opened them to look me over.

"How can I get in touch with you?" I asked.

The man in the leather jacket answered for him. "He's usually right here, or you can ask for him in the lobby at the Sunshine." He was referring to the Sunshine hotel, a rather infamously skeevy SRO, near CBGB's.

"Alright, we're good. Thanks Sammy."

As we walked away, the man in the leather jacket told me what I'd been suspecting; that Sammy did not speak English.

"He speaks money," he said.

We rejoined Chelsea, and his friend with the cane.

"Alright, we got to go," the man in the jacket said. "We're on a deadline." He didn't elaborate. "It was nice meeting you girls. Don't make that driver of yours too crazy."

We offered them a ride, but they declined.

"I figured out who you remind me of," the man with the cane said to Chelsea, who he had obviously developed an affection for. "Edie Sedgwick. You're not a toothpick like she was, but something about the eyes and the face. Maybe it's the hair. And the driver. The reincarnation of Edie Sedgwick."

"It was nice meeting you girls," the man in the jacket repeated, with a smile. "But I'm curious. Why'd you ask us?"

"I like your look," I said.

Like walking death.

It was the truth.

Kill Your Idols

Both Gene Gregorits and I are bicentennial babies, and judging from what he's written online, and in his various books, I think we had a similar adolescence. We were both obsessed with the Sex Pistols. We both made 'zines, and put classified ads in the back of *Maximum Rocknroll*, looking for attention from the opposite sex. We both loved underground movies, and read *Film Threat* magazine in its heyday under the editorship of Chris Gore. And both of us, intrigued by what we read in Gore's coverage of New York City's Cinema of Transgression, became involved with the filmmaker Nick Zedd.

It was through Nick that I met Gene. Though it would probably feel less shameful to claim that I was initially drawn to Nick because of his DIY production values, or the stable of underground personalities he cast in his films, with age and a bit of maturity, the need for highfalutin' rationalization has fallen away. I was initially attracted to Nick because I thought he was gorgeous. At least he appeared to be, in the pictures that I saw of him in *Film Threat* and in his book *Totem of the Depraved*. He resembled a sort of dark prince Hayden Christensen, and would be shown draped alluringly amongst tree branches in a leather trench coat, or completely naked, his hair perfectly mussed and his penis on his kneecap, with a Bolex camera handcuffed to his wrist. Nick was a genius at self-promotion, and his look was perfectly tailored to the fantasies of young punk film fans from the suburbs. Almost all of the early attention the Cinema of Transgression received was due to Nick and those memorable images, and the articles he wrote himself, about himself, using aliases like "Orion Jeriko" or "Rufus Jacoby." Nick was equal parts filmmaker and pin-up.

I didn't even need to seek Nick out. At twenty-one, I moved to New York City, and ran into him at a John Waters books signing. He was all by himself, and I went up to him and introduced myself. He was friendly, but spoke with an awkward response delay that made me think of autism and Andy Warhol. This was before the internet was ubiquitous, and things like people's birth dates were accessible at your fingertips, and I was surprised to see that Nick was older than I had thought. I still found him to be incredibly attractive, with his thick, bright red hair, and ghostly white pallor. (Writer Jerry Stahl once described Nick as "a real 'look at me, I'm dark' experience," and the description always stuck with me.) Though I'd come to the book signing with a boyfriend, I accepted his mumbled invitation to come to the premiere of his new film at Anthology Film Archives. I really wanted to have sex with him.

The film was Nick's short Warhol homage *Why Do You Exist*, and it was having its premiere at Anthology Film Archives as part of The New York Underground Film Festival. Nick and his entourage of actors and actresses took up a few rows of seats in the front of the theater. Nick, clad in a floppy velvet hat and Amber-vision sunglasses, waved me over to their area, and I immediately felt intimidated and out of place. Everyone in his group was older than I was, and much more arty-looking. One person a few seats down in my row caught my eye, mostly because he looked more like the people I knew in my everyday life: like a punk rock boy, in black jeans and a band t-shirt. I knew that Nick would have film-world schmoozing to do after the movie, and I wondered if maybe this boy would be willing to hang out with me. He seemed the most approachable.

A large woman with a French accent kept turning around in her seat next to Nick to glare at me. As soon as she'd sat down, Nick had stopped turning around and acknowledging me. This added to my sense of discomfort, but I didn't have much time to dwell on it as the film started. I watched as the people I was surrounded by were reflected on the screen. There was the French woman, snarling at the camera, smoking a cigarette and removing her blue bathing suit. The underground cartoonist Mike Diana, the first artist ever to receive a conviction for obscenity in the United States, stared blankly into the camera, his blonde hair limply hugging his skull. Performance artist and musician Nick Bohn, who would tragically die a few years later of a drug overdose, rubbed something on his chest that looked like blood. Then Nick's camera zoomed in on the limp penis of a good-looking young man with dark hair and a sharp jaw as he sat naked and spread-legged in a chair. It was the boy from my row, in the black jeans and t-shirt. I looked over at him quickly. I thought he looked squeamish.

When the film ended, there were people everywhere, congratulating one another, writers for the *New York Press* and *Village Voice* asking filmmakers and members of the audience for comments and blurbs. It was clear Nick's attention was going to be elsewhere, and I didn't see the boy in the black jeans anywhere. I decided to leave, and made my way over to Nick to say goodbye. Out of nowhere, like some kind of omnipotent bodyguard, the French woman appeared in my path.

"He's busy," she said haltingly. She gave me a look that made me feel like I owed her some kind of explanation.

"I was just going to leave," I said nervously. "Could you tell Nick I'll call him?"

"Why?" she hissed.

"I don't know..." I stammered. Over her shoulder, I could see Nick watching our encounter, yet he made no attempt to come over and intervene. Instead, he moved his hand to his ear quickly, making a gesture that indicated he would call me.

I wasn't an idiot, and it all seemed so unnecessary. I felt like I was sneaking around by omission, like I was sneaking around without even meaning to sneak around. I wasn't expecting Nick to be my boyfriend. The French woman was obviously his girlfriend.

I went outside and lit a cigarette. Things had just gotten complicated in a way that I hadn't anticipated. Among the throng outside of Anthology Film Archives, I spotted the boy in the black jeans.

"Hey," I said. "I saw you in Nick's movie."

"Oh yeah," he said. "You were sitting near me." He held out his hand. "My name's Gene, and you just saw my cock."

I laughed. I thought he was cute. "My name's Fiona," I said. "I don't want to put you on the spot or anything, but does Nick have a girlfriend? I think I just had a weird experience."

"He has a roommate," Gene said, using his fingers to put air-quotes around the word *roommate*. "I lived with them for a little while. One piece of advice," he said. "Her name's Sophie, and she's violent. She hit Nick with a baseball bat once. I think we're leaving to go to Mars Bar, do you want to come?"

"No," I said. "I think I'm just going to go home."

"I work at Kim's Video. If you're ever around, come by and say hi."

"Ok," I said. "Nice meeting you, Gene."

***

Soon thereafter, Nick and I consummated our relationship on the floor of his downtown storage space, amongst his film props and movie posters. I would see Gene on and off when Nick and I went out, sometimes at Trailer Park, a theme night at Coney Island High, where the Notorious *BOB* would make hamburgers and chocolate sundaes on her breasts, or at Max Fish, where we'd do coke in the bathroom. Nick loved to gossip about his friends, and most of what I learned about Gene at first, came from Nick, a most unreliable narrator: Gene and his wife had lived with Nick and Sophie, after moving to NYC from Pennsylvania. Nick had suggested Gene's wife get a job as a stripper, and already intimidated by city life, she'd fled from both New York, and her husband. Nick showed me an essay he had written where Gene's wife was a minor character. He'd changed her name to "Zoe Cliché."

Over the course of our relationship, I learned that the only people Nick seemed to genuinely like and respect were his personal icons, the musicians, writers, and artists who had influenced his films. He seemed to dislike everyone else, but some people he disliked more. It was as if he put everyone he knew into two categories: traitors, and traitors-to-be. It's like black magic when you view people through that kind of prism, always with a degree of distrust and suspicion, because it affects the way that you treat them, and your ideas about them often become a self-fulfilling prophecy. A prophecy that I feel like I'm living up to, as I write this.

***

In 1999, Nick began working on the film *Ecstasy in Entropy*. The original premise of the film had something to do with politically-minded dancers in a strip club, but the plot mostly went out the window as the camera rolled. The film became about jiggling female flesh in its most visible forms: women dancing, and women wrestling. Gene and I were in the film alongside Taylor Mead, Will Keenan, Nick Bohn and Annie Sprinkle.

Originally, I was just supposed to play a bartender in the club, one who fought with Nick Bohn and broke a prop bottle over his head, but then Nick came up with what he thought would be a great idea for another scene. He wanted all the women on set to take their clothes off and undulate in a big mass on the elevated stage. It was almost like he tried to call your bluff, like a dare, or a game of chicken: how ART were you, and what were you willing to do to prove it? He'd procured a stunt penis for the film, one that could secrete fake jism from a hidden pump, and decided that one of the actresses should fellate the fake dick, and get sprayed on her face with fake cum. The actress was hesitant to do the scene, but agreed, having no idea how much fake cum Nick planned on spraying all over her. The filming was hard to watch, and seemed to go on forever, as Nick saturated her face, hair, and chest with the cream-colored liquid. Her boyfriend was on the set, and stood next to her, holding a towel as she cleaned the fake cum off her body. She was clearly upset, but stayed on the set, and continued with the filming.

Nick, with a sheepish smile on his face, slunk off to help with the lighting for the big orgy scene.

***

When I saw the film for the first time, years later, I was surprised at how little of it I was in. The big orgy scene had to be scrapped due to a problem developing the film at the lab, and my bottle-over-Nick Bohn's-head scene was gone, too. It almost seemed metaphorical for my relationship with Nick: whatever it was that we had, boyfriend/girlfriend/lover/piece of ass on the side/ it went on for over a year, but it was really a year of nothing. Though Nick moved in with me at one point, it didn't feel like we were ascending to some benchmark in our relationship, and when he moved out, I wasn't upset. Though he told me he loved me once, I didn't really believe him when he said it, and I don't remember him saying it ever again. Though my name is on the credits of the film, you really see me for only half a minute. I'm behind the bar, in a low cut dress, with a patron in sunglasses and a leather jacket sniffing coke in front of me. The patron is Gene.

***

In the end, if there ever really was an end, Nick and I just fizzled out. There was no big boom, no big show of dramatics. As I said to Nick once when we were fighting online, *I just stopped showing up.* But I never stopped thinking about Gene. For some reason, he had captured my imagination. I had noticed that Nick had started talking about him more harshly, it seemed like they weren't friends at all anymore, but I couldn't get a real feel as to why. Gene had been writing for a small New York City paper, and I'd wondered if Nick's feelings had stemmed from something related to that. Not because writing for the paper was some illustrious job, it wasn't, but because Nick liked to think of himself as the only *real* artist in all of his relationships.

Before I'd moved to New York, I'd had two short movies on a compilation of female filmmakers. The filmmaker Sarah Jacobson had a trailer on one of the compilations, and when I saw that she was going to be in the city, showing the whole film, I got Nick to go with me to see it.

Sarah and I didn't really warm to each other. One of the short movies I'd made was a parody of riot grrrl culture and poked fun at all its sacred cows with silliness and gross-out humor. Sarah was referring to this when she said to Nick, "I can see why you two get along."

"What does that mean?" Nick snapped.

Sarah seemed to choose her words carefully. "Well, your films seem to share a similar... *sensibility.*"

"Don't compare her *videos* to my *films,*" Nick snarled. "What an ignorant thing to say. You obviously have no idea what you are talking about."

I didn't take my "videos" all that seriously, nor did I expect anyone else to, but it struck me then, as it does now, as the most basic of courtesies, especially if you are in a relationship with someone, to either *pretend* like you do, or just keep your mouth shut. Nick never felt like he was under this kind of obligation to anyone. He seemed to view this kind of lack of sensitivity as the spoils of what he considered to be his genius.

The real reason for Nick's bitterness towards Gene did reveal itself. Her name was Lydia Lunch. In his writing, Nick cast Lydia as "the one who got away," and their relationship as one big star-crossed *would have, could have, should have.* If only he'd had more money. If only he'd gotten to Europe faster. Lydia was the only one who ever *really* understood him. She was the only one who was his equal. He had even made a film of Lydia in Ireland and used the recording she'd made breaking up with him as the soundtrack.

In the same way that Nick was my pin-up of transgression, I suspect, at a young age, Lydia was Gene's. Lydia was living on the other side of the country, so it wasn't like Gene could just run into her downtown, the way I had with Nick. They started writing letters to each other, and a relationship formed. I'm sure hearing about this made Nick crazy. If Lydia was his equal, and she would deign to be with Gene, did that make Gene his equal?

Nick and I were done, and I was ready to make my move on Gene. I brought my friend Susan with me, as moral support.

Inside Kim's Video, a boy and girl sat behind a counter, on stools.

"Can I help you?" the boy asked.

"Is Gene here?"

"Gregorits? No. You didn't hear? He moved to California, to be with Lydia."

I'd finally gotten it together, and Gene was gone.

Kill your idols.

Thoughts on the Shit Show

On August 3, underground writer Gene Gregorits was arrested for sexually assaulting a seventeen-year-old girl. He'd posted about her the night before on his Facebook page: he put up a picture he'd taken of her, under a Facebook status that read, "The teenage porn star tourist cunt has arrived appx. 8 mins late. And I still fucking hate her. I am going to do things to this woman that Cletus from Moose Snout would not do to the family cow in the depths of a meth binge." The post was removed after his arrest, but many people took screen shots of it while it was up. I have promoted Gene's work for years, always under the auspices that there is something so important about pushing boundaries when it comes to art. I wrote the following essay about my feelings about his arrest, and the disillusionment I'd been feeling beforehand as someone who had been such a big proponent of his writing.

Sick of being decent, he craves another crash. What reaches him except disaster?—Frank Bidart

Author Gene Gregorits recently did a small tour of New England with Lisa Carver, where he was promoting his newest book, *Do You Love Me: The Gene Gregorits File*. The first night of the tour, a naked Gregorits accidentally-on-purpose slashed open his forearm with a knife, the resulting wound requiring close to 50 stitches. Anybody who is friends with Gregorits on Facebook has seen pictures of the festering wound, above or below photos of his injured cat, posts pleading and bleating his friends for rent money, and a relentless barrage of diatribes against:

1. Those who haven't bought his books

2. Those who have, but haven't written reviews about them

3. Women

4. Other writers and artists who have taken a more conventional path to success, and been rewarded for it.

I haven't seen the video of the show, as YouTube keeps flagging it, but from what I've been told, most of the attendees either ran off, horrified, or dipped their just-purchased copies of his books in his blood as a souvenir as Gene was taken to the hospital. On his Facebook page a few days later, a somberly reflective Gregorits seemed saddened by the audience's reaction, which I found surprising. Connecting the dots on the Gregorits persona, one would have thought he'd be proud. People always take souvenirs of that which thrills them, and what else could Gregorits have been seeking when he'd disrobed and grabbed the knife? Police had to stop souvenir hunters from removing Clyde Barrows' fingers after he'd been shot. There have always been rumors that a plaster cast was made of John Dillinger's dick at the morgue. Surely in someone's curio cabinet, there is a piece of 1990's toilet paper with GG Allin's fecal matter on it.

It's like Bill Maher on the 9/11 hijackers. Say what you want, but self-mutilation—like commandeering a plane, then flying it into a building—takes guts, unless you have dead nerve endings. Cutting yourself fucking hurts. Gregorits' cutting was the on-purpose, the depth of the wound was the accidental.

Though Gregorits has written 12 books of varying quality—some great, others slap dash and badly in need of editing—the book he was promoting with the tour is one that others, myself included, wrote about him. *Do You Love Me? The Gene Gregorits File* is in the tradition of Daphne Gottlieb's *Fucking Daphne*, though

Gregorits would probably claim his is the first of its kind, because he does that: speaks in bold generalizations, in assumed hyperbole, about everything. This begs the question— just what is real about Gregorits' persona, and what isn't? There are some things that I hope aren't.

***

I hope this isn't too confusing. What you just read is the beginning of an essay I started three months ago, but never finished. If I had, it would have been the fifth time I'd written about "agitator author" Gene Gregorits. I know what I was considering writing; I still have my notes. That description, "agitator author," would have been new, at least for me, but some of my other planned descriptions, like "madman writer" would have been recycles. I was going to lineage Gregorits' writing with Louis-Ferdinand Celine, and Nelson Algren, as Gregorits himself often did. I made a note to mention the psychic fluke of the double "G" initials: G(ene) G(regorits) and GG (Allin). I would have written something about "appreciation only after death, because we never reward the artists who really challenge us in life." (In another essay I wrote about him, I called this "the ultimate straitjacket.") I was becoming a broken record. I was writing Gene Gregorits Mad Libs. I didn't finish the essay.

When I was twelve, I had a poster on my wall. It was a drawing of Sid Vicious, and in messy scrawl around his body, it said:

"Undermine their pompous authority. Reject their moral standards. Make anarchy and disorder your trademarks. Cause as much chaos and disruption as possible but don't let them take you alive."

There was a little stamp on a corner of the poster that said it was "a Sid product," authorized by "kind permission of Sids Mum, Mrs. Anne Beverley." I think, I knew, even then, that Sid didn't say the words attributed to him on that poster. I did an internet search, just to be safe, and can find no video commemorating the moment, or interview transcript connecting those words to Sid's mouth. Sid Vicious was 21 years old when he died, and it's not unfair to say that he was not particularly articulate (though the murdered and maligned Nancy was, and in Nancy's mom's book, she included a very coherent letter and poem sent to her by Sid after Nancy's murder). It's a pretty safe bet that the words on that poster were crafted either by Malcolm McLaren, or some suit and tie guy who knew that their anti-authoritarian sentiment would appeal to a certain kind of disaffected youth, of which I was, and I know Gene Gregorits also was. I wrote the quote from that poster all over my school books, like voluble, long-winded graffiti. I slept under the poster for close to three years. I opened my eyes to those words in the mornings, and dreamed next to them at night. But that's who a shit show should appeal to: the innocent, or the ignorant. Those are the two groups who can get away with it, without much excuse, or justification. They get a pass.

I should identify here exactly what I mean when I say "a shit show." The other description I will be using is "pet savage" but I'll explain what I mean by that later.

What is a shit show? A shit show is, at its barest bones, the five point plan outlined on that Sid poster. A shit show is no rules. A shit show is a wad of spit, a rich, frothy, tubercular loogie, in the face of cooperative morality, and by "cooperative," I mean the morality that says, you don't fuck with me, and I won't fuck with you: the most basic of all 'you must have neighbors in this world' moralities. A shit show is nothing is sacred, no woman and children first, no special provisions for the elderly, it is the killing of all sacred cows, even the vegan ones. A shit show is chaos as religion, because "God is dead." (Nietzsche is often popular with pet savages because his writings can be twisted ever so slightly to back up their chaos theories.) A shit show all by itself is usually a crime. A shit show when put on paper or to music, is no longer whirling, twirling chaos. Then it's art. We can take it on the road, and we can travel with it. Have shit show, will travel. Somewhere in all of this, as a token gesture, is the idea that the ugliness of a shit show is supposed to tell us something about the beauty of the world. Like the idea of a lone daisy sprouting from the ruins of a nuclear holocaust.

I'm not the only person no longer innocent nor ignorant to still carry a torch for a shit show, there are many like me, and I've come up with a profile of those of us who continue to do so, well past our sell-by dates. We hold back, when we wish we didn't. We fantasize probably a million times a day about telling different people to fuck off—from the top, down: a big "fuck you" to our spouses and partners, our bosses, our children (remember, no one is safe), our parents, that person in front of us at the supermarket, the police (duh), anybody who infringes upon us, but we don't. If we are artists ourselves, we fantasize about the comeuppance of our fan base for not acknowledging our work—at least in a way that actually benefits us—and artistic institutions for not acknowledging our genius, or for not acknowledging us at all. We have an innate disdain for any authority over us, yet we grudgingly comply. If we do have an outburst, we work to smooth things over, often at the expense of our feelings of self-worth and dignity. We hate the high personal cost of doing business in this world. To quote the band Alice Donut, we have "revenge fantasies of the impotent."

The shit-shower, who, from here on, I will refer to as the "pet savage," we believe makes none of these concessions. And as a reward for his not conceding, we in turn relax our own expectations of his behavior. He is our "pet" because we would never tolerate his kind of behavior from just anyone. We've given him a pass. Usually, there has to be some kind of artistic, or philosophical ideology attached to him, as part of his package. In a sense, he is an avatar for the rage inside of us, bubbling just below the surface. "He's mad as hell," but the difference between him and us is he's actively doing something about not taking it anymore. When Hollywood shows him, he is usually represented by a man having an extreme "break": William Foster in *Falling Down* or Travis Bickle in *Taxi Driver*. He is usually shown alone, because no one else has the guts, and how could he partner with anyone anyway? When nothing and no one is sacred, he has no one to answer to. While we are rooting him on for slipping the ties that so effectively keep us in our places, that keep us conceding— our fear of consequences, and often, our conscience—we forget (or ignore) that these things also do much to keep us human.

Those of us who venerate a shit show also have a low threshold for boredom, and if there is one thing a shit show is, it's never boring. In the weeks before Gregorits' arrest for alleged sexual assault on August 3, we were no longer friends on Facebook, but I still read his page every day.

We who venerate a shit show romanticize the ruffian. In the same way that we say "out of the mouths of babes" we want to think that people who have lived outside the boundaries of cooperative society have something to teach us, are enlightened. "Out of the mouths of ruffians." And often, they do. People will ask me why I devote so much of my writing to the period of my life when I was a drug addict, and the short answer is, the duress of those situations will often lead people to drop their masks and show who they really are. And if not who they really are, then parts of themselves that they normally try hard to conceal. I know I learned much over the period of time when I was drug-addicted and desperate. The Jean Genets, the Herbert Hunckes: they are the enlightened fringe dwellers. But the pet savage takes it one step further with his disregard.

Like me, Gene started off as a venerator of the shit show. A pretender. On his Facebook page, sometime this past July, Gene posted a letter he had sent as a teenager to *Film Threat* magazine editor Chris Gore, asking Gore if he wanted to see a video of Gene cutting himself. This was an early overture, Gene looking for an in. It was also one of the reasons that I thought that I could relate to Gene so much. I wrote about it in the essay I wrote for *Do You Love Me*. I had met Gene through the filmmaker Nick Zedd, when we all lived in New York City, in the late 1990's. I knew Gene had met Nick through the fan letters he had written to him after watching his films. Gene and I are the same age, and I imagined him, like me, growing up feeling alienated and isolated in small town suburbia, dreaming about New York City as some kind of cradle of disaffected creativity. I wrote in the essay that Gene and I had the same teenage pin-ups of transgression, boy/ girl version: Nick Zedd for me, Lydia Lunch for him. I believed Gene and I had the same origins when it came to influence. I still do.

There is a clearly lineaged influence to an act like the one Gene's life became—a shit show— cutting yourself for public consumption, berating and provoking your audience (usually verbally), attacking women (often physically)—Sid Vicious, GG Allin, Jim Goad: the next generation builds on the one before it, and with the pet savage it's the same. When Gene decided to become a savage, instead of just writing about them and chronicling their bad acts as he'd done with his zine *Sex and Guts*, he decided that his paradigm would be part GG Allin, part Jim Goad: both of whom made misogyny a big part of their act (I'm conflicted as to whether or not I should use "act" or "art" here) and both of whom did jail time for crimes against women. Ugliness as lineage. It's hard to imagine aping the uglier, if not the ugliest parts of people; it's hard to imagine that you might be venerating ugliness when you stop to think about it, so we chalk it up to "persona." It's not real, it's just provocative. It's not real, it just makes you think. It's more palatable. More refined. The shit show is an art form that requires its fan base to adopt a coping strategy.

I have always been a girl who was intrigued by ugliness. The more refined, the better. I don't know why. Maybe it goes back to that profile, and my own feelings of powerlessness. Growing up poor, my parents not talking to each other for years, having to flee the house with my mother and siblings when my dad came home drunk, I'd tune myself out to those 1980's Geraldo "Satanism in America" specials and read paperbacks from the spinner rack at the supermarket on Ted Bundy. But it was always ugliness from a distance, at arm's length, and whenever I teased it closer, I would catch myself, and push it back. I wrote letters to notorious killers, like Richard Ramirez, but when he actually wrote me back, I snapped out of it, and didn't respond. When I'd written to him, I sent him a picture of my chihuahua. I tried to play cute with a serial killer. There was a disconnect there. Some kind of delayed reaction. There still is.

If I'd gone to one of GG Allin's shows, I'm sure I would have hidden in the back, which still would have been dangerous, because a woman at a shit show is almost always a target. As one pet savage builds on the bad acts of the savage before him, this is the hallmark that has remained non-negotiable. There is no place for women in a shit show. It's a glass ceiling that has yet to be broken. It may be the distinguishing mark of the paradigm.

In Gene's zine, *Sex and Guts*, he interviewed all the outsider art legends. He knew the history of the shit show, and knew that to be lineaged in the same context, he had to build upon their bad acts, or at least remain level with them. Bukowski is the "loving" woman-hater, the gross old man who slaps a girl on the ass when drunk, maybe calls her a "cunt"— but offers apologies, and maybe flowers and cheap chocolates, when he sobers up the next day. You meld the bard misogyny of Bukowski, with the caustic anger and learned vocabulary of Jim Goad, with the lunkheaded punk and disorderly of Sid Vicious, with the egotistical, I owe nothing to no one of Nick Zedd, with the brute force "my body is paper" of GG Allin, and you have Gene Gregorits. It's paint by numbers.

Gene's medium was what was different. The internet. However I feel about Gene now, however he chose to live his life, however he chose to treat other people, especially women, however much of his real self he gave over to the shit show and to becoming a savage, Gene Gregorits is a good writer. He is such a good writer, that at times, I've been jealous of him. Gene's shit show promulgated the idea that he was living and writing at the height of a mess, a mess so messy he couldn't get a regular book out of it, only a book of mostly bitingly smart Facebook status updates. When I was at the height of my mess, I could never have written as well he did with so much going on, which led his behavior back to persona. In all of its ugliness, Gene's talent as a writer is very real. The book of Facebook updates, *Fishhook,* attests to that. Even at his worst, the intelligence was still there, which just made everything that much more infuriating. Here is a person who had so much articulate talent, but had somewhere along the way decided that his contribution to the shit show, his pet savage pet cause, was going to be his mistreatment of women.

I don't want to go off on too many tangents, but I will say that Lisa Carver has earnestly shown herself to be a proponent of outsider artists for years. She's performed beside them, in her travelling punk opera *Suckdog*, and written about them in her popular zine *Rollerderby*. I'd be curious to hear how she would report on her experiences as one of the few female artists in a male dominated paradigm. We know what they've said about her: In the GG Allin story, she's the contemporary of his that he wanted to rape and murder on film. In the Gene Gregorits story, she's the *Vice* writer who put him on the map to a larger audience, become his friend, and vocal supporter, wrote a book with him, went on tour with him, and is commemorated for her help bringing his work to a larger audience in video tirades where he calls her things not worth repeating. In the Nick Zedd story, she's two words, according to Nick: "an idiot."

Even when I was still gawking at Gene's Facebook page, and starting a new essay about him, I was messaging friends about how uncomfortable his posts on Facebook were making me feel. I even thought about reconciling the uncomfort with *more* writing about him: I thought about writing about the uncomfort itself, and the conflict I was starting to feel about promoting his work. I wanted so much to believe in the romantic and intellectual promises of the shit show that I saw myself becoming a borderline Gregorits apologist.

On May 29 I wrote to a mutual friend in a Facebook message:

I don't want to meet up with him or see him again, ever. I don't want much to do with him at all, but I can't look away.

On June 4:

I want to delete him so badly, I see through all his persecution complex Lenny Bruce bullshit, but there is also a really gross side of me that wants to see what happens, and finds inspiration in how angry and disgusted he makes me feel. It makes me hate myself and feel like I need to get a fucking life.

It's disturbing to think I was having conversations like this instead of just saying enough is enough. Instead of just saying, this isn't fucking art anymore. This isn't something that I'd accept from any man who didn't put paint on a canvas, or words on a page, or lyrics to music. It had gone too fucking far. Gene Gregorits wasn't some anger muse for me. Art had become the excuse.

On May 29th I sent this message to a friend:

My typing is a mess.

What I am trying to say is I hope he doesn't hurt someone to become a footnote in some anthology about outsider artists in the early part of the 21 century.

In spite of Gene's devil may fucking care attitude on his Facebook page, I think he cared very much. Much of what was on his Facebook page was contrived, with friends backing up the bullshit he posted behind the scenes. I think this made it easier for some of us to think that most of the ugliness he posted was also contrived. He'd never gone off on me before. His comments on my Facebook page, when he left them, could be a bit leery-eyed: I saw him he do this with other women writers, as if he thought by sexually talking down to us, it would look like he was putting us in "our places," typical priapic he-man macho-man bullshit. But this was the public Gregorits. In private messages, at least with me, he was always on point. A few weeks before he was arrested, he'd heard that I was working on a list article about Lydia Lunch's ex-boyfriends, and though I'd written about him so many other times, with his help and cooperation— this time, he demanded that I show him what I was writing. Ironically enough, there was nothing for me to show. I'd thought about putting him on the list, out of some misplaced sense of...I don't know...loyalty? But in the end, I'd decided against it. He was demanding to see something from me that didn't exist. And even more ironically, I didn't want to hurt his feelings and tell him that, so I lied. I lied and told him that he *was* on the list. Things snowballed from there, with him messaging me that "pissing him off was not a good idea." The whole exchange was ridiculous, but it was time for a falling out. It was past time. I hadn't cut the ties myself, and fate seemed to intervene.

Later, I posted this on Facebook:

One of the ugliest things about me is that I can still be seduced by a shit show when it comes to art, and I use "seduced" purposefully. I know better, but still I get sucked in, and I hate it about myself. I fool myself with canned justifications that there is something so, so, necessary about a lack of boundaries and a finger in the face to all societal norms, especially if the person's words are put together well, or their musical accompaniment is catchy. It's not a fair representation of who I am, or how I feel. It's actually grossly hypocritical, and contrary to how I feel. A lack of boundaries does not equal art. Godard was wrong. The first edit is not the first lie. The first edit is often the concession we make for the protection of the human heart.

It's so funny to me to think I'd lied to Gene to protect his feelings.

The Whore Box

I tripped over the Whore Box. Looking down, and seeing it there at my feet was quite a shock. I wondered if I should call the police, or the bomb squad. I had lived in New York City on September 11th, and was well-indoctrinated, "if you see something, say something," though I never did. A few weeks after the attacks, at the height of the anthrax scare, I found a small piece of paper on the sidewalk, folded up like a child's fortune teller. It was covered in strange symbols, and its folds were lined with white powder. I took it back to my apartment, cut a fat line of the powder, and sniffed. Nothing happened. I kept what was left in a drawer in my kitchen until I showed it to my sister, thinking she would marvel in its esoteric weirdness with me. Instead, she grabbed it from my hands, and flushed it down the toilet.

This time was no different, though I put my lighter in my pocket, and didn't light my cigarette, as a precautionary measure. The Whore Box was a Sketchers shoe box, the company's logo obfuscated with black marker, as if whoever had left behind was afraid of an accusation of copyright infringement. I found the box on the porch of the women's halfway house where I worked weekends. No one had rung the bell, and I found it only because I had gone outside to smoke. There was no name on the box, no indication to whom it was directed. Just the five scarlet letters, scrawled out in red lipstick across the box's top: *W-H-O-R-E.*

This was not much of a clue, as everyone at the house was a *whore*. I was a *whore*, my boss was a *whore*, my boss' boss was a *whore*. Most women don't end up at a state-financed halfway house for the treatment of drug addiction without having been a *whore* at one time or another. *Whore* is the burden of women who do desperate things for drugs. When it's used by someone to whom it's been applied, in acknowledgement of another to whom it's been applied, it can show affection, and function as a term of endearment. The stigma works like a unifier, and the melioration of the word is an attempt to rob it of its power. Out on the porch, on the Sketchers box top, it was clearly *whore* in the more traditional sense: crude, shameful, meant to degrade.

Lifting the lid on the box, I was confronted with the evidence locker of a broken relationship. A medium-sized teddy bear with a red bow tie told of a trip to a carnival, and two balloons popped, not three. I poked the cheap bear's belly, and could feel the lima-bean beads inside. A half-emptied bottle of men's cologne did not make the box quarters fragrant. Had it been emptied, then refilled with piss? What looked to have been correspondence, written on yellow-lined paper, had been ripped to tiny, minuscule pieces. A disfigured red lipstick in the same shade as the WHORE on the box's lid rolled around loosely; at first glance, because of its cylindrical shape, I thought it might be a bullet.

Under a pair of knotted underwear that strangled the pieces of a decimated cell phone, I found a laminated Mass card, and then I knew for whom the box had been left. I recognized the name and face of the woman on the card. She was the grandmother of a client of the halfway house named Autumn.

Autumn had come through the halfway house once before, a year earlier. She was a twenty-two-year-old heroin and crack addict whose unhealthy habits had yet to rob her of her good looks and youthful air. The love and support of her grandmother had also helped to keep her face smooth. Some women go to jail, have sex with strangers in the backseats of cars, and lose something much more real and affecting than their dignity. They lose their ability to laugh at themselves, and at the world. The ones who can still laugh afterward, who don't go hard forever, nine times out of ten, are the ones that remain somebody's beloved daughter, sister, mother, wife, little girl. If the family can hang in there, she will stand that much more of a chance.

The first time Autumn had come through the halfway house, she'd been the ideal client. She'd come from jail, and had been cooperative and low-maintenance, focused on getting a job and her own apartment. Then one day, she went outside to smoke a cigarette, and disappeared. New London was her old stomping ground and provided plenty of temptations. Did she just give in? No one knew, but it was a common scenario. Each week, clients of the halfway house simply went to the bodega, and didn't come back. The New London Police were familiar with Autumn, and weren't concerned. On top of the drug charge that had landed her in the halfway house in the first place, they'd also arrested her in the past for prostitution. But Autumn's grandmother *was* concerned, and launched a crusade.

She was doing so well. I'd never seen her more focused in my life. She was turning over a new leaf. It was a boyfriend who got her on all the drugs when she was just a teenager. She didn't have the easiest time growing up, you know. She came to live with me after her mother went off the deep end. I raised her as my own. She'd done a year of college for nursing. Why does the New London Police Department not care about my granddaughter? Please, if you have Autumn, let her go. If you can hear me, Autumn, Grammy loves you.

When the police just rolled their eyes, Autumn's grandmother went to the media. This sweet old woman was desperate with worry, and sick with breast cancer. They put her on TV, and wrote about her concern for her granddaughter in the local papers. Searches for Autumn were organized. Based on a tip, a lake a few towns away was dredged. A matted length of brown hair extension was found. Her grandmother said she thought it was Autumn's. What did it mean?

Nothing, the women who had lived with Autumn at the halfway house said. *It meant fucking nothing. It meant some dumb bitch went swimming and lost her weave.* The media coverage of Autumn's disappearance made some of the women angry. They didn't believe any harm had befallen Autumn; outside of any harm that she was most likely doing to herself. She'd told a few of her housemates that she could not stop thinking about smoking crack. She was probably holed up in some apartment somewhere, geeked out of her mind. She'd resurface eventually, they said, adding resentfully, that if it had been any of *them* who were missing, no one would have cared. And they were probably right. Autumn had her grandmother, both naïve and determined, and with her ivory skin, and full set of bright, white teeth, at least physically, she was the idealized at-risk woman: pretty and young. Unlike many of the women at the halfway house, Autumn's years of hard living hadn't caught up with her yet.

Two months after Autumn disappeared, she did resurface, in jail. She'd been picked up again for prostitution. Because she was still on probation for the drug case that had put her in the halfway house in the first place, the additional charge meant she was returning to jail. She did less than a year at the women's prison, and was released back to the halfway house. While she was in jail, her grandmother succumbed to breast cancer. It was her Mass card inside the Whore Box.

"He's a fucking freak!" Autumn said. She was seated across from me in a swivel chair in the staff office, the Whore Box open in her lap. It was late on Saturday afternoon. On the weekends, not much was expected from the clients of the house, and I'd woken her up for the first time that day.

"Who?" I asked. "Who left this for you?"

"*Trevor.*"

She held the broken cell phone in her hand, and attempted to unknot the underwear wrapped around it. "I can't believe he stole my fucking underwear!"

"Who's Trevor?"

"That older guy who's always picking me up. He helped me bring in all those grocery bags last weekend, you met him. Tall guy, pornstache?"

It had been a quick encounter, one of many I had on the weekends when the clients' friends and families came to visit. I had probably assumed the man was Autumn's uncle, or some other relative, if I'd thought about it at all. A few of the women continued their paid sexual relationships while living at the house. If their friends and family couldn't provide for them, how else were they going to get money for the things they needed until they found work? The halfway house provided food and shelter, and basics, like tampons and shaving razors. Used clothing was donated by various non-profit agencies in the area, but everything else, the women had to provide for themselves. This meant they needed money fast.

"What is he so angry about?"

"Who knows. He was my grandmother's friend. He saw the stuff on the news when she was looking for me, and called her, offering to help. When I was arrested, he started putting money on my commissary and writing me letters. I don't know. He seemed all right. He took me shopping, and out to eat. He bought me the phone." She held up the broken remnants. "I can't believe he took my underwear! And my bear!"

"There was nothing more between you two?"

"No! He's like sixty! Not that that's stopped me before. I gave him the number of the payphone here after I got out of jail, and he starting calling, talking about what a great woman my grandmother was, and how helping me was a way for him to honor her memory. He offered to do things for me, so I let him. I must have left the phone in his car last night. I've been sleeping all day, so I didn't notice. I bet he went through my text messages! I met a guy at the Narcotics Anonymous meeting on Thursday night. Really cute Hispanic guy named Hector. He's living at the men's halfway house on Mercer Street. It's funny, Trevor calling me a *whore*. He told my grandmother that was the reason he wanted to help her find me. Because people act like women like me are disposable."

"If you weren't having sex with him, how did he get your underwear?"

"Like I said, I let him do things for me. Last weekend, he offered to do my laundry. It was after Sunday night curfew, and I couldn't leave the house, so I just passed him my laundry basket through the door. He must have taken them then."

"I'm wondering if I should call the police."

"Please don't! That last thing I want is any more contact with the police. I'm infamous around here. When I see policemen on the street, they laugh at me. *Back from the dead*, a cop said to me the other day. I'm not afraid of Trevor. I'd rather not have him in my life anymore. He was saying weird things to me."

"Like what?"

"Things intended to make me feel bad, but make him look good. Things like," Autumn affected the tone of a man giving a serious speech, "*People know all about you around here, Autumn, and are going to judge you, but I never will. No man will have the guts to date you, he may fuck you, but he'll never bring you home to his mom...*"

"Autumn, Trevor is an *asshole*. Don't *ever* put up with anyone talking to you like that."

"I needed him. But what he was saying is also true, I know that. Any guy who Googles my name isn't just going to find a Facebook page. I loved my grandmother. I feel horrible about what I put her through. I should have just called her. All it would have taken was one phone call. But I didn't, and this is what happened. It's all out there for anyone to find. I'm missing prostitute Autumn Fields, the hooker who came back from the dead..."

"In this community, we all have crazy backstories, Autumn."

"*In this community*. In the AA/NA/jail/social service community. What happens when I want to go outside this community? Every employer nowadays does a web search. My name is hippy-dippy enough as it is, but there are also pictures of me."

"You haven't even been back here a month yet. Give it a little while. It's asked that you make a decent effort to find a job by your third month here. Who knows what opportunities might present themselves to you by then."

"Um-hum."

"I'm going to write an incident report. Do you want to keep any of this?"

"Just the Mass card," Autumn glanced down at the picture of her grandmother before putting it into the pocket of her sweat-shirt.

"Oh! I have the X CD I said I'd burn for you," I said, hoping that the CD might lighten the mood as I reached into a drawer on the side of the desk.

Her first time coming through the halfway house, Autumn had heard me listening to the band X in the office. "I haven't heard Exene's voice in so long!" she'd said. I'd offered to burn her the CD then, but had kept forgetting, and then she was gone. Autumn and I liked a lot of the same music, mostly punk bands from the 1970's and 80's, that we were both too young to have ever seen play live in their original incarnations.

"Thank you!" she said, opening the plastic cover and looking at the album artwork I'd photocopied. She leaned over to give me a hug. "I can't believe I slept this late. The Seroquel they have me on is really kicking my ass. I'm going to go take a shower, and take my time getting ready for the meeting."

AA and NA meetings, especially the ones on the weekends, were treated like social events by the clients. Most of the women went, putting time and effort into their appearances, doing their hair, and giving their outfits careful consideration. I'd done it too, when I'd come through the house as a client, four years before.

Autumn got up from the chair, and moved towards the office doorway, stepping through the threshold that connected it with the house's dining room. A few clients sat at the dinner table, playing cards.

"I'm surprised Hector hasn't called," she said.

"I was just looking for you," an older woman named Rose replied. "A man called for you like five minutes ago. I tried to take a message, but he didn't want to leave one."

The pay phone was a constant bone of contention amongst the clients. If you answered it, there was an understanding that you were willing to put in the effort to find the person the call was for, sometimes a major undertaking, as the house had three floors, a front and backyard, and a basement. I glanced over to the pay-phone in the hallway. A woman stood talking on it, with two other women lingering impatiently nearby.

"I won't be able to survive here without a phone," Autumn said.

"You can use the phone in the office," I offered quietly, hoping that the other clients wouldn't hear, and accuse me of favoritism. I did a quick check of the med drawer and the filing cabinet that contained all of the client paperwork. Both were locked, so I left the office, giving Autumn privacy to make her call.

I had let Autumn use the phone because of what had happened with Trevor. But I might have been guilty of showing her favoritism. It was hard for me not to. She reminded me of me.

****

A few hours later, I was sitting at my desk eating dinner when Rose approached the open office door.

"That girl's sketchy. You know that, right?" she said, standing in the doorway.

"Who? Autumn?"

"Yeah. She's never here. She's always out running around. You know what she did to her grandmother, right? You know her grandmother died?"

"Yes. She had breast cancer."

"The stress of having that girl for family didn't help. Hector, that guy she's after, he has a girlfriend. Autumn needs to watch herself."

"Does Autumn know that he has a girlfriend? Did you tell her?"

"No. It's not my place. She shouldn't be getting involved with guys from the Mercer Street halfway house, anyway. It's obvious what they want. They're not even here for 30 days."

This was true, though I suspected Rose might have been twisting the truth to be self-serving. The men's halfway house on Mercer Street was only a three week program, while our halfway house was a much longer one: the women could sometimes stay for more than a year, it was up to the state of Connecticut to decide. Ironically, the quicker a woman found a job, the sooner the state mandated it would no longer pay for her care, the ideology being that she was now in a position to support herself. The fact that most of these jobs were barely minimum wage didn't play into the state's calculations.

"Well, I don't think she's a mind reader, Rose."

"Can I use the computer really fast? Just for a minute. I'm waiting for Grace and Sarah to finish getting dressed, then we're going to the meeting."

I got up from the desk and went into the living room to type in the password that unlocked the web browser. It was on a timer, and would clock out after fifteen minutes unless the password was re-entered.

As I cleaned off my dinner plate in the kitchen sink, I heard the printer come to life in the other room. Soon afterward, the back door slammed shut as Rose, Grace and Sarah left for the meeting.

A few minutes later, Autumn came down the stairs. She was wearing a short black skirt and a t-shirt with Debbie Harry's face on the front, her hair pulled back in a loose ponytail. The weekend before, she had pierced her nose in the 2nd floor bathroom, forcing a small stud through a hole that had closed while she was in prison. There is a lumescent glow attributed to a person's first few weeks clean, and Autumn had it. She looked vibrant and healthy, though her glow was probably the result of her first few weeks out in the fresh air, as she'd gotten clean in prison.

"Okay, I'm off," she said, leaning over to sign her name and the time into the client sign in/sign out book. "Wish me luck."

"If you see him, stay away from him, Autumn. Don't even give him the chance to apologize to you."

"Not with Trevor, silly. He went to meetings with me a few times, but I don't think he'd show up on his own. I'm not worried about Trevor. I meant wish me luck with *Hector*."

"You should ask Rose about him. I think she knows him. I wish they would have waited for you, so you wouldn't have to walk over to the meeting alone."

"I'll be fine. Rose knows Hector? She was there when I met him, and didn't say anything. I think she has some kind of problem with me today," Autumn brought her arms up to her shoulders in a resigned gesture that implied, *What can you do?* "Whores!" she said, then gave me a quick wink, and went out the door.

****

The woman who I split the weekend shifts with was on vacation, so I had agreed to work from 8 AM Saturday morning until 4 PM Sunday afternoon. 8 of those 32 hours could be spent sleeping along with the rest of the house, and more than 20 of them could be spent reading, or watching television with the clients, if I chose to, so it was hardly laborious. I had light paperwork to do, but most of the time I felt like a glorified babysitter. I'd sometimes tell people when they asked me about my job that I'd been hired as a guarantee that 911 would be called, if ever their services were needed. The truth was, I was hired because I was considered a success story, a former client of the halfway house who was still clean several years after leaving the house. Every member of the staff was. If Autumn stayed clean, once she left the house, she could apply for a job, too. The pay wasn't great, but there *were* places where she could work where her past wouldn't be seen as a disqualifier. But she'd been right; all of those places were within "the community."

At 9:30 pm, I was sitting in the office flipping through a magazine when Grace flew through the door.

"Something happened at the meeting," she said. Some clients seemed to put a bounty on being the first to report dramas, both real and imagined, to the staff. It appeared Grace had been running. "People were passing around a paper about Autumn. She started crying, and left."

"Did you go after her?"

"I don't know her that well. Somebody said they saw her get into a car," Grace studied me for a moment. "Rose did it. That Trevor guy said he'd pay her to print something out, and pass it around the meeting. Is it true that Autumn killed her grandmother?"

"Are you serious? If Autumn killed her grandmother, she'd be in jail. Her grandmother died of breast cancer."

Grace tugged on the sleeve of her sweater, like a child.

"If she doesn't come back, do you think I'll be able to keep this? It's Autumn's sweater. I really like it. I got so many compliments on it at the meeting tonight. If she doesn't come back, do you think I'll be able to keep it?"

****

My first thought was to call my boss, but I was hesitant, as she hated to be called on the weekends. I didn't blame her. She worked Monday through Friday, and deserved to have her weekends drama-free. It would have been premature to call her anyway. Both Rose and Autumn had until midnight to return to the house without consequence.

The browsing history on the computer showed that Rose had been looking at an article from a local newspaper. It contained a black and white picture of teenage-looking Autumn, smiling, in a button down shirt, in what looked to be a yearbook photo. The headline of the article read, "WOMAN SEEKS INFORMATION ON MISSING GRANDDAUGHTER." The boldface below the picture of Autumn identified her as "MISSING PROSTITUTE AUTUMN FIELDS."

Over the years that I worked at the halfway house, I'd become close with a handful of clients, and a few of them had become friends that I stayed in contact with after they left the house. It was hard to maintain a professional relationship, the things we discussed while watching television, or eating meals, lent themselves to camaraderie: prostitution, jail, abuse, disease; topics not easily broached with the uninitiated, free of judgment.

I wasn't particularly close with Autumn, but I could relate to her.

I had first gone into rehab when I was seventeen years old, and for years, had the distinction of being the youngest person in my various treatment programs. While I was considered too old (the first time I'd gone into treatment, by only a month) for the programs offered to juveniles, I was too young to understand the challenges many of the women faced. I had no children lost to the black hole of DCF, no husband who I loved, but desperately needed to separate from. I always had visitors who brought me clothes, food, and cigarettes. I was blessed to still have my youth and my family, but these blessings alienated me from some of the women. My family was hardly rich, but they might as well have been, by virtue of so many of the women being so deprived. Care was a currency, and in care, just by the nature of my having it, I was wealthy.

One visiting day, while I was a client of the halfway house, a big, burly woman who I lived with there named Daphne sat down next to my mother while I was in the bathroom, and demanded that she give her twenty dollars. Later, when my mother told me that this had happened, she said she hadn't felt intimidated by Daphne. She said she had given her half the amount, ten dollars, not because she'd felt that she to but because she'd felt *bad* for Daphne. She'd noticed her on other visiting days, sitting in the living room, watching TV, all alone. Worried my mother would now be considered a mark, we never stayed at the house again when she came to visit. I had women I considered to be my friends take money, clothes, and other objects of value from my room. Often times, in treatment, as in jail or on the streets, there is an inverse hierarchy to the haves and have-nots, and the haves are on the bottom. In the sorority of sickness, the premium is often on the suffering, because that's all you have to compete with. Through your tales of woe and despair, you make your bones. How can a person expect to change when their self-worth and identity is so tied up in how wrong things have gone for them?

Sitting in the office, I looked into the garbage can, at the innards of the Whore Box inside of it. Without thinking, I took the stuffed bear from box, picked up a pen from my desk, and started stabbing it in the stomach again and again. A mix of brown beans and gauzy cotton spilled out onto the desktop. I assumed that Rose would be out until curfew, spending her pay-off on real cigarettes instead of rollies, and a nice meal, after so many months of the halfway house's food stamp fare.

I was wrong. A few minutes later, she came through the backdoor defiantly.

"I'm sure Grace told you what happened," she said, coming directly into the office. "I don't care that she was upset. I don't give a shit. I'm sick of these bitches who have everything, and treat everyone else like shit."

"How did Autumn treat you like shit, Rose? What did she do to you?"

"How do you know what she did or didn't do? You aren't here during the week. You don't know. She's in and out of here every-day, acting like this place is her fucking hotel. She never has to wait in line for the payphone. Never has to dig through a garbage bag of donations for something to wear. Tonight's the first time she's had to walk to a meeting since she's been here. She thinks she's a prin-cess."

"You're jealous."

"I'm not jealous. I'm doing her a favor. She thinks she's spe-cial, but she's just a whore, like the rest of us."

"Don't try to mask what you've done, humiliating a person for money, as something righteous."

"Oh please. Everyone here was a prostitute, and women talk about it at meetings all the time. So what, even her whoring's spe-cial? What's the consequence? Am I on restriction? If I am, it's worth it."

"If Autumn doesn't come back tonight, that's on you."

"No, that's on *her*. If she doesn't come back, it's because of the guilt she feels for killing her grandmother."

"You need to stop with that."

"No. I know people who were in jail with that girl and saw the letters she'd get from her grandmother, when that old woman was in the hospital *dying*. After what she did to that woman, she still wrote to her! Still sent her money. If she's really off drugs, that guilt is going to be catching up with her real quick. If she doesn't come back tonight, it will be because of that, not because I printed out some article. People at meetings don't care anyway."

"You knew she was sensitive about it."

"Whatever. You just like her, that's why you care. I see you in here talking. You're just another person who makes things easy for her. I'm toughening her up. She needs some suffering. She's spoiled."

"So tell me Rose, what has suffering ever done for *you?*"

****

Besides being younger than everyone else, and still having people in my life willing to come and visit me, and bring me money, and cigarettes, I had another strike against me when it came to making friends when I was in treatment: I was considered a freak. I had brightly dyed hair, and piercings. I dressed in a manner people considered to be funny, and listened to loud, screechy music. At one treatment center, I had my roommate request to have her room switched. She told the head counselor at the facility that I made her feel uncomfortable, that my presence in our room was an affront to her religious sensibilities, the implication being that I was some kind of Satanist. Rehab for me was always an end of the road motel. When I was desperate enough, and out of options, I'd agree to go, but most of the time, once I started to feel better, I'd decide that I wasn't that desperate, and leave.

I met Sam at the treatment center where my roommate asked to have, and got, her room switched. Between groups, the patients at the facility would sit outside on a picnic bench, smoking cigarettes, laughing, and gossiping together. I'd usually sit a little bit removed from the group, under a tree nearby, reading, or listening to music on my Walkman. In spite of the alienation I felt from the other patients there, I was doing well. It was my third time in treatment, and the longest I'd ever stayed. I didn't know if I wanted to stay clean forever, but my mind had started to clear, and I felt optimistic about the future, or at least I was starting to think about having one. There was a commercial that was popular on TV at the time: over scenes of darkening despair, a disembodied voice said, "Nobody says, 'I want to be a junkie when I grow up.'" After snorting heroin for the first time off the floor of a Subway sandwich shop bathroom, my friend Chelsea and I had started talking back to the TV whenever the commercial came on, that *we did*. But my plans had begun to change. Getting high no longer just felt good. My mother had kicked me out of the house, and I had started to get dope sick. Chelsea had overdosed, and was in treatment at a different facility. I decided that I was going to stick the 28 days out. I was still only 18 years old. Maybe I'd try doing something conventional, like what other people my age were doing. Maybe I'd go to college. It wasn't like my original plan of becoming a junkie was going to go anywhere.

Sam introduced himself to me one day after morning mediation. He was funny, and though no one else at the facility had given me a chance to prove it, I was funny, too. He was 50 years old. Born and raised in New Haven. He'd been a Black Panther, something I found to be infinitely fascinating, and asked him question after question about. When crack-cocaine came along in the 1980's, it derailed his life. When he asked me about my plans for the future, I told him that I was thinking about going to college, and maybe doing something with writing, and he didn't laugh at me. Instead, he showed me poems that he'd written in prison, and we became an unlikely twosome: the punk rock junkie and the ex-

Black Power crackhead. He stuck up for me to the other patients, and I began to feel more welcome, not so much of an outcast.

Sam was always flirtatious with me, but it felt harmless. We would talk about music, and the worlds we ran around in outside of treatment. He would ask me questions about my hair, and my clothes, some of which were short, revealing, and tight.

One day, we were talking about my piercings. At the time, I had my nose pierced, but I also had my nipple pierced, and my clitoris. When Sam asked me about the piercing in my nose, I told him about the other piercings that he couldn't see. Maybe it was naïve of me. All I know is I didn't think about it twice. He was my friend, and I wasn't ashamed of having the piercings. Why wouldn't I be honest with a friend, if I wasn't ashamed?

He wouldn't let it go though. He made sexual comments about my piercings over and over again for the rest of the day. I tried to brush off and deflect his comments, but they didn't stop.

That night, after the NA meeting, as we walked back to our rooms, Sam said that he was going to sneak out of his room that night, and sneak into my room. He said he was going to flick my piercings with his teeth.

I panicked. I had demurred to all of his come-ons, tried to change the subject, but nothing had worked. I was afraid that he was really going to sneak out, and somehow get past the staff. But in case he was only joking, I didn't want him to get into any trouble. There was a young technician at the facility who I had a slight rapport with. He worked at night, and sometimes when I couldn't sleep, I would get up, and he and I would talk. What I was trying to accomplish seemed reasonable to me at the time. I thought I'd come up with a way for Sam and I to stay friends, to keep him out of trouble, and out of my room. I told the technician the truth, minus the sexual harassment I'd put up with all day. I told him about telling Sam about my piercings, and what Sam had said about sneaking out, but stressed to him that I was sure that Sam was only joking. My plan was to downplay the threat I felt, but say enough to put the idea into the tech's mind to keep an eye on my room.

The night came and went without a hitch. No Sam in the moonlight, no sounds of disturbance in the hallway, or outside my door, or window.

The next morning, as we all filed into the group room for morning mediation, the vibe from the staff was off. The staff members sitting in the front of the room to lead the mediation seemed distracted and tense. Sam came in with the other men, and smiled at me, just like any other day, so I knew that he and I were fine. Whatever had happened, it had nothing to do with us.

The head counselor of the facility, an older, buttoned-up look- ing woman, the same person who had granted my roommate's room switching request, came in, and sat down.

"It's been brought to my attention that some of you have been coupling off, and encouraging inappropriate behaviors. Fraterniza- tion is one thing. We don't condone it, but we realize that some- times, in intense environments like this, men and women will be- come close. Come-ons and sexual enticements are something else entirely. I don't know where the idea would come from that it would *ever* be appropriate to talk with *anyone* of the opposite sex about intimate parts of your body..."

I looked over at Sam. His eyes looked like they were about to fall from his head. I could tell by the look on his face that what she was saying hadn't come from him. It could only have been the male tech's interpretation of what I had said to him the night before. He'd thought I'd been coming on to Sam, and by coming to him to talk about Sam, he'd thought that I'd been coming on to *him.*

The counselor had been talking about me, and turned to face me. But it didn't matter what she was saying. I'd been doing well. I'd lasted the longest I had, in any facility, ever. I had actually been thinking about doing things *differently* this time. She had given me all the reason I never knew I needed *not* to try. Humiliating me, in front of people, who, for the most part, didn't like me anyway. Painting me as some kind of freak show seductress. I packed my bags in my mind as she went on.

All these years later, I don't blame the counselor, or the technician. I don't blame Sam. I could have sucked it up. I could have tried to defend my way of thinking. Ultimately, it was my choice to leave. What I do know is that it would take me 10 more years to get back to that place where I'd been up until that moment, up until that moment I'd been put into the whore box, *willing to try.*

As Rose turned and left the office without answering my question, I had a feeling Autumn would do the same thing.

****

The phone rang at five of midnight.

"Autumn," I said. "Come back. Everyone's in bed. If you're late, no one will know. I won't tell anyone, and I won't put you on restriction."

"I'd never let you do that. It wasn't just what happened at the meeting. Coming from jail, that's hard. I just need a little bit of time to fuck around."

"But you're going to go back to jail."

"Maybe not. I'm with my mom, about an hour away. She's doing really well, and knows a lot of people in the program around here. She thinks she might be able to hook me up with someone who can help me with the court."

"You're not with Trevor?"

"No! Fuck him! New London is too small. I know everyone there, and everyone knows me. It never would have worked. I know Rose is talking a lot of shit about me right now. Some of it's true."

"I want you to make good decisions, Autumn. I don't want you to waste all the time that I did. I don't want you to get hard, and mean."

"Tell the rest of the staff that I'm sorry. You guys have all been so nice to me. I'll be down sometime during the week to get my stuff. Damn! I meant to get it before the meeting. You didn't empty out the garbage can in the office yet, did you? The bear in Trevor's box, it's mine, from when I was a little girl. My grandmother gave it to me. I'd spilled coffee on it, and was going to wash it. Trevor must have taken it from my laundry basket when he took my underwear..."

I looked down at the bear in the garbage can, its guts hanging out everywhere.

"I'm so sorry, Autumn. I already emptied it into the dumpster outside. You know how the garbage truck comes on Saturday nights...I think I can hear them outside, right now..."

Final Notice

"As soon as the collection agencies discover he's dead, they are going to drain that bank account," John's sister, Rebecca, said. "I'll write you a check for the balance, minus a few cents to keep the account open, and date the check for a few days before he died."

Rebecca had been handling all of John's finances while he'd been sick, and I'd been impressed by how well she could sign his name; it looked a lot like his signature. Forgery is one of those refined talents drug addicts have that don't translate well into any other world. One of my refined drug addict talents had been rifling through the dresser drawers and pants pockets of people asleep in the same room.

"Deposit it immediately," Rebecca warned. "Collection agencies monitor the Social Security rolls to go after the estates of the deceased. They're relentless, the vultures."

She dropped off the check that afternoon. It was for $287. My son's father had died a few months shy of his fifty-first birthday with less than $300 in tangible assets. It was just a number, a bunch of pennies, dimes and nickels, but it still made my heart hurt.

John's addiction, like most addictions, was cyclic. It seemed like he was constantly building things up only to tear them down. He'd move into a new apartment, make a big production of decorating and buying the furniture, then stop paying the rent and the furniture would all end up out on the curb. He'd lose his license, get it back, buy a car, and install the mandatory ignition-lock Breathalyzer, then sell the car to local drug dealers once he blew numbers and the engine would no longer start. He was like a Buddhist in that he held on to nothing. He couldn't. His life was in the scattered closets and basements of family members and halfway houses across the country.

I told myself I would not spend the $287 dollars. I would just leave it there, in the bank, until our son was old enough, then with great gravitas, I would give it to him and I would say, "This money is yours, from your father." For some reason, I had come to see the money as cash, cash straight from John's worn leather wallet, in the same denominations he had touched and fingered.

Before he died, John and his sister had started the process for him to collect Social Security/Disability. It had all happened so fast—only a month between his diagnosis and death. He'd been in a lot of pain, especially at his job, where he was expected to lift very heavy things, and he had taken to wearing Lidoderm pain patches all over his back. One morning, he got out of bed, and that every-day exertion was enough for him to snap a rib. He couldn't work with a snapped rib, couldn't ignore the intense, live-wire pain of a snapped rib, so he went to the hospital, and was diagnosed with Stage 4 cancer, just like that. Each rung on the ladder towards death had a holiday. He was diagnosed at Thanksgiving, in hospice by Christmas. Dead a few days after New Year's. The money in John's bank account was the remainder of the first and only Social Security/Disability check he had ever received.

I talked to John every day on the phone after we found out he was sick. At first, I was in denial. I thought all he needed to fight the cancer was chemo and a positive attitude. I thought the most important thing was that he did not use his diagnosis as a reason to drink or get high. My denial dissipated after our first visit post diagnosis. His downward slope was staggering. It was if he had assumed the costume of a sick person overnight—grey sweatpants, a perfect match for his pallor; plastic, open-toed sandals with white tube socks. Personal appearance had always been very important to John, in his vanity he had never lagged. With his life's valuables in garbage bags at his feet, he'd check himself into rehab in a starched button-down shirt and hounds tooth blazer. He'd often be mistaken for a counselor at the facility, not the dope-sick or DT'ing patient he actually was. The cancer must have been festering inside him for a long time. It was as if that snapped rib had served as the final barrier to its surfacing, and he had no choice but to cozy himself into the wardrobe of his new role.

Another reason John may have been so frequently mistaken for a counselor was that he *had* been a counselor; he'd been *my* counselor. John was the second or third person I met when I checked myself into detox for heroin in 2003; he'd done my intake paperwork. One of the beauties and curses of many rehab facilities is that they often hire former clientele as staff. It's a boon for the clients, to have staff who can relate to their issues so intimately, who have faced many of the same challenges, but sometimes these people are still very early in their sobriety, and their decisions, like John getting involved with me, reflect that. I had no idea how early in sobriety John actually was. When we met, he'd told me he hadn't drank or taken a drug in over three years; that is what he told everybody. In reality, John was still smoking pot a few times a day and crack whenever he could manage to slip away for the weekend. Eventually I found out the truth, but by then, I was in love with him. So I left the halfway house I was living in, and moved in with him. Soon, we were getting high together.

***

One of the last times I saw John before he was diagnosed, I had done something stupid. I am not always very good with bills. It is not so much a poverty issue as it is a scattered-brain one. "Final Notices" with their red banners and dramatic upper case lettering seem to get my attention best. The "Final Notice" that came from Connecticut Light and Power, for some reason, did not. John was in the area, doing well, and came by the house to visit our son. CL&P makes you suffer when you forget to pay a bill, and even though I paid the past due amount minutes after everything went dark, they still wouldn't return the power until the next day. John could have given me shit for this, could have really relished the moment, me, the fuck-up for once, not him, but he didn't. Instead, he spent the night and we played Uno with our son by candlelight. The next day, he helped us get rid of everything in the fridge that had gone bad without electricity. We had fun, letting our son throw rotten eggs off the deck. John's back was hurting him, and he would frequently lie down on the couch and doze off. I could make out the outline of the Lidoderm patches on his back through his shirt. He was looking for a better job, was about to get another car, was looking to move out of the halfway house where he'd been living. He hadn't drank in over a year, or done coke or dope in a year and a half. I believe that these were honest and true calculations. He didn't give me shit for being a flake about my bills. This was all growth. We didn't know. We would know in two months, and he would be dead in three.

"Try to stay on top of these things, Fiona. Just pay your bills as soon as they come in."

"I know, I know," I said. "Though it would have been fun to stay in a hotel with a pool."

"I don't think your boyfriend would approve of you and I staying in a hotel together," he said.

"We could have gotten separate rooms."

"What a waste of money, Fiona! Just stay on top of your bills!"

***

Every week, I get paid on Friday. The Friday after I receive John's final check, I imagine the monies in my bank account like entities on a segregated street: on one side is my money, my work-earned money, on the other side is John's $287. The denominations cannot be mixed or intermingled. John's money means something, is symbolic of something; this smart, handsome man who worked great jobs, and shitty ones, who drove expensive cars, and trash heaps. Whatever that something is, it's for our child.

That Friday, after work, I go out to the mailbox and discover a bill from Comcast. It is a "Final Notice," and our television service is about to be cut off. The bill is for three months of service. I can pay a little—$90, or I can pay the whole thing, $287.

I think about talking to the Comcast operator on the phone. "Yes, I would like to authorize the transfer of $287 from my bank account, just not from the money in the account from the check pre-dated Jan. 4th. You may have to call Bank of America about this. I know it sounds complicated, but your letter is all red in the headline, which means time is of the essence, so you are going to have to put your metaphysical thinking cap on, and work with me. You can have the money, it's all there. You just can't touch a certain portion of it, understand?"

***

Completing John's new sick-bed wardrobe was the heavily medicated look in his eyes.

As soon as the cancer in his liver, pancreas and esophagus was discovered, his new doctors went about treating his pain correctly, with substances much more powerful than the Lidoderm pain patches he'd been using; substances like fentanyl, oxycontin, dilaudid, and morphine. Substances, from the same family of drugs— opiates— that for the duration of our relationship, right up until my pregnancy, had been our lives' primary pursuit, that had made the importance of everything else pale in comparison. John had spent the majority of his lifetime trying to clean up from the ravage that his want for them had brought. Now that he was dying, he had permission. There was a part of me that was jealous. But there was always a part of me that was jealous of John; I had gotten clean for our son, while he hadn't.

In Narcotics Anonymous they talk about *not yets*. Stolen from your grandmother? *Not yet.* Sold your body? *Not yet.* Done a jail bid? *Not yet.* I got clean to turn the *not yet* of losing our child into the closest thing to a *never*, and this meant leaving John when our son was two months old. He had stopped coming home at night so we wouldn't fight and he wouldn't have to lie to my face about being drunk or high. He'd also developed an affinity for gambling. I was taking a bath with the baby when he came to the doorway to tell me that he was going to a casino to double the money that his father had lent us to help with the bills. I was still on maternity leave, and we were close to three months behind on the rent. After he left, I packed up all our stuff, mine and the baby's, and my mother came and picked us up. I was still in my bathrobe. Though we never lived together as a family again, there was a quiet part of me, a very, very quiet part, that I've only come to know now since his death, that held onto the hope that maybe one day we would. For me, this is one of the hardest things about John's death. Losing this very, very quiet hope.

***

John used to say I was "senti-*mental*." The way I hold on to everything; notes, drawings, cards; I can infuse a piece of garbage with supernatural powers, and call it a good luck charm. He, more than anyone else, by the nature of his cycle, knew that you can't take it with you. Drug addicts have to part with things all the time; some of those things are inane, some of them profound.

I need to pay the Comcast bill and I know I cannot explain my ridiculous "senti-mental" feelings about the money in my bank account to the operator.

It's par for the course. Drug addicts have to part with things all the time.

$287 to Comcast, in denominations real or imagined, qualifies as inane.

The loss of John will always be profound.

Disavowing Victim

I don't like the word "victim." Though it's an accurate description of my role in certain situations, when it's used to describe me as a person who has experienced sexual assault, I think it gives the perpetrator even more power. *Here is the new identity you have foisted upon me. I am your victim.* "Victim" refers to our inter-tangled relationship, and whenever I can, I want to be as separate from you as possible. I don't want to share a word with you.

I'm not the first person to feel this way about "victim." When AIDS first emerged in the 1980s, people with the virus where described as "AIDS victims." Some in the affected communities disavowed the term for similar reasons: they thought it was disempowering, that it was giving their lives, their identities, over to the virus. They were still alive, still fighting to live, but felt that they were being described as if the virus had already taken them. Their preference was to be called "People with AIDS." I don't have a concise alternative to offer to people who have experienced sexual assault.

There are others things about the lexicon of sexual assault that bother me. I try to rectify this in the language I use, or don't use, when I write about the times I have experienced it. I will either try to describe those situations, and the dynamics that were at work, or if I can find no other way around it (meaning, mostly, I'm aware of some kind of time constraint), I will use words like *victimize*. *Vic-*

timize works for me. It's a verb, and connotes transition. It's also something one *does*, as opposed to something one *is*.

The first time I was sexually assaulted, I couldn't even identify that I had been. I knew what sexual assault was, but only in the way that it was shown in movies or after-school specials. I thought that it involved implicit violence, and loud, verbalized resistance, and perhaps even Jodie Foster. All of my points of reference were cinematic, or explained to me by health teachers to involve creepy uncles or "stranger danger." It's funny to me to think that I was ever that literal and naive. There were other factors that played into my delayed identification of the assault for what it was. Namely, my feelings about myself at the time. My dislike for myself.

The person who sexually assaulted me was named Trey Roberts. He was a senior in high school at the time, and I was a freshman, 15 years old. The year was 1992. Though my friends and I couldn't recognize it then, Trey hung out with us because people his own age kept him at arm's length. He was good looking, and funny, in an uncomplicated way, and had a car, and weed connections. As a friend who could do things for us, he was a score. He dated three of my girlfriends consecutively. I had no interest in Trey Roberts as a boyfriend, which was convenient, because the politics of being Trey Roberts meant that he never would have been interested in me as a girlfriend. The generalized male consensus about me at the time was that I was funny and smart, but not very attractive. Boys like Trey tolerated me because I was part of the package of pretty friends. Because of this, I ended up spending a considerable amount of time around him, and he would often turn to me for relationship advice.

He and I were alone at a local swimming spot the day that he assaulted me. We were waiting for Trey's girlfriend, one of my best friends, to arrive, and Trey was complaining to me that she wouldn't have sex with him, that she was, in his words, "a prude." I remember him saying this to me as if he believed I held some sway over the situation, like I could lead her to reassess her decision, and in turn "put out." I had no such power, and wouldn't have used it for the benefit of Trey Roberts nasty cock, even if I did, but he must have suspected something about me, that turned out to be true: that I wouldn't repeat to my friend what he had said about her, at least verbatim— that I could be trusted to keep secrets for him. And he was right. I never told anyone, until years later, what happened next. But it wasn't out of shame, or fear. It was out of ignorance.

I didn't try to fight off Trey Roberts that day at the swimming spot because I had never thought of sexual assault like this, as happening between two friends, as they did something innocuous, like hanging out, waiting for another friend. I also didn't try to fight Trey Roberts because I didn't want his girlfriend, my good friend, to stumble across us, or to hear us, so I wanted what was happening that I didn't want to happen to be over as quickly, and as quietly, as possible. I knew that if anyone were to find out what had happened between Trey and I, it would be viewed as cheating, and I would be blamed.

Because I couldn't yet identify what had happened that day as sexual assault, in my gut, on a visceral level, what bothered me about it was the inequity of it. Not only was Trey bigger than I was, and able to utilize that strength in order to force me to comply, in the court of public opinion (meaning, our group of peers and friends), his ideas and definitions of the situation mattered more than mine. My "no" hadn't mattered to Trey Roberts, nor would it matter to anyone else. This made me angry and resentful, but I never felt afterward that I had been changed in some way by what Trey Roberts had made me do.

And there was this: I disliked myself so much at that age that I tried to interpret what had happened that day in a way that could make me feel better about myself. I tried to tell myself that Trey had forced himself on me because he found me as desirable and attractive as the friends of mine that he dated. It's hard for me to write this, but I remember wondering—after accepting that what was happening was going to happen whether I wanted it to or not— whether or not I looked ugly to Trey Roberts as I knelt there in the dirt, his torso hovering above me.

A dominant narrative has an intimidation effect. When your story is different, you are more likely to keep it to yourself, rearrange it, or dismiss it entirely, for not measuring up. As ideas about what constituted sexual assault became more broad and inclusive as the 1990s moved on, introducing concepts like date and acquaintance rape, and *no* (always, no matter what*) means no*, what didn't change was the motif that sexual assault should damage you, or at the very least, alter you in some profound way.

I have felt, sometimes, when I've told my story, that this is what the audience wants from me. Like a blood lust: a "broken" lust. Maybe it makes for a better narrative arc, the collapse, followed by the empowerment, the phoenix-like rise from the ashes. Maybe it's about reparations: a sense of reparative justice becomes that much more imperative when a person has clearly been hurt. But because I can't tell my story this way, I have been made to feel that I must be even more profoundly damaged than I realize.

When I was 17, I tried heroin and fell in love with the high. It's a high that is easy to fall in love with. I was in and out of treatment for most of my twenties. While I was a client at a woman's halfway house, I saw a therapist who spent a considerable amount of time with me going back and forth over my history, looking for the uncle, the cousin, the family friend, whose actions against me had made me into the drug addict that I had become, and who had made me, what my therapist said, was "cold" and "disconnected" when I talked about being sexually assaulted. The therapist was somewhat relentless: we had to find the man, he said, because it was his actions against me that had led me to medicate my pain with drugs, and later, to work in the sex industry.

I became aware that other things were different about my story when I found myself feeling alienated by the way people would react to it, especially when I wrote about it, online. It made me feel uncomfortable to hear "you are so brave," over and over again. When I told a friend that I felt this way, she told me that I was just being "humble," but that wasn't it. People's offers of solidarity seemed predicated on the notion that I needed them to help hold me up. I wasn't telling my story to feel whole again, but the implication that I must have been seemed to be everywhere: the implication that I *must have* been broken because I had been sexually assaulted seemed to be everywhere. Trigger warnings implied that there were things I could no longer handle. Out of one side of their mouths, people were telling me I was brave and strong for being candid about what had happened, only to tell me out the other side that there were things that I was just too fragile for.

I told myself, again and again, to just ignore these feelings. To just accept that the *intention* behind the response came from a good place. But the irony seemed intense: I felt no hesitation about talking about being sexual assaulted, something that I had been told again and again *should have* been hard for me to talk about, but was hesitant to address my sense of alienation about people's reaction to the assault. But I couldn't ignore my feelings, because I knew how much perpetrators of sexual assault got off on the idea that they had broken us. I felt like to kowtow to this identification, to call myself a victim, or let other people refer to me as one, was to make porn for them.

As the 1990's rolled on, at the same time that ideas about what qualified as sexual assault broadened, sex-positive feminism came into vogue, and women became sex workers not just out of last ditch economic necessity, but out of a want for empowerment, and sexual freedom. "I can sell my body if I want to," Kathleen Hanna sang, in her band, Bikini Kill. Courtney Love, Kathleen Hanna, Lisa Carver, Cookie Mueller: these were the women that I looked up to, all of whom had been sex workers. I wanted to be like them, strong, I imagined, and confident in my sexuality. Also, as a young woman who had come out of two plus decades of thinking of herself as "the ugly girl," I was curious to see if men would be willing to pay for my company. I had started using heroin, and sex work conveniently provided me with money, every day, that I could use to buy more. I could be high and feminist at the same time, I told myself. It sounded like the dream.

What happened to me was this: I was sent to see a client, and after he paid me, he became rough. It became clear to me that he was going out of his way to hurt me. I told him to stop, or I was going to leave. He said, you will stay until I finish, or you will give me my money back. He must have had some idea about the behind the scenes workings of escort agency sex work, how, after I had called the agency to tell them that I had arrived, and been paid, from there, I became responsible for the agency's money, whether their fee came from the client or directly from me, they didn't care. The compassionate, understanding den mother willing to hear my side of the story was a fallacy, as was the bodyguard/ brute waiting somewhere nearby, ready to back me up. The reality was I would be on the line to pay the agency myself. So, I decided, I will just get through this. As my time with the man continued, I figured out what he wanted. Every time I told him to stop, told him how much he was hurting me, his breathing quickened. He wanted to make me cry. He wanted to *see* me cry. I think of this man whenever I write about sexual assault. It shapes the language that I use. I never gave him what he wanted. In the event that he, or someone like him, might be reading this, I won't give it to them now. This might be the primary reason I disavow the word "victim." I know how much perpetrators of sexual assault enjoy thinking of us that way.

Live Through This: Twenty Years in Love with Courtney Love

I can't say this about many things in this world, but I can say with a degree of certainty that I remember the exact moment when I became aware of Courtney Love's existence: I was at my friend Chelsea's house.

Chelsea was a year younger than me, and her parents had allowed her to drop out of high school to take correspondence classes. My friends and I would skip class to go hang out at her family's cavernous house, where her parents were never home, and the refrigerator was always stocked with expensive organic foods. Chelsea would spend the school day there, all alone, dying her hair with different colors of Manic Panic, and sometimes doing her schoolwork, always with the TV set to MTV in the background. My friends and I had a snobbish air about the music we listened to. We subscribed to the adolescent idea of "the sell-out," a concept often espoused by those who don't know much about the real struggles of the world. We thought of ourselves as 16- and 17-year-old punk rock purists, who listened to only the real deal, punk bands from Washington, D.C, or the Bay Area of California, bands that we told ourselves would never affiliate with major labels or "go mainstream" in order to promote their music. Chelsea was the only one in our group of friends who had no time for such posturing. She liked what she liked when she liked it, and this included bands like Soundgarden, Pearl Jam, and Nirvana—all getting heavy rotation on MTV at the time. One day, my boyfriend Mark and I left school early to hang out with Chelsea at her house. Her dog started to bark as we came through the door.

"Shut up!" Chelsea yelled in our direction. Her eyes were glued to the TV screen.

"Today, Nirvana frontman Kurt Cobain married Hole singer Courtney Love in Hawaii," announced MTV VJ Kurt Loder. On the screen, a montage of Kurt and Courtney followed, then snippets of Courtney playing with her band Hole.

With her ripped dress, bleached blonde hair, and candy-apple red lipstick, Courtney looked like a 1920's movie star who'd gotten dressed for a fancy event, then neglected to change her clothes or wash off her make-up for the rest of the week. Her look said something about beauty in ruin, but with a little girl innocence, conveyed by the Mary Janes on her feet and the pink plastic barrettes in her hair. A journalist would later refer to Courtney and Babes in Toyland singer Kat Bjelland's war of accreditation for this look as "The War of the Schmatta," *schmatta* being the Yiddish word for rags. Just the quick visual of Courtney relayed so much; playing with tropes of sexuality and innocence, she looked like the Little Match Girl with a guitar. I thought she was one of the most glamorous looking women I'd ever seen. For all my screams of "sell-out" along with my friends, I'd always loved Hollywood, especially old Hollywood, and considered the battered copy of Kenneth Anger's *Hollywood Babylon* that I'd stolen from a used bookstore to be one of my most prized possessions. Visually, Courtney was the physical hybrid of two worlds I worshiped at: one of them secretly, the other much more openly.

"Fucking bitch!" Chelsea said, throwing the TV remote at the screen. Though Chris Cornell of Soundgarden was Chelsea's primary Northwest corridor crush, she still had a soft spot for Kurt.

"Who fucking cares," my boyfriend Mark said. Mark's parents had recently moved to New York, but his father had done well enough in his job at a large corporation to afford to keep a house in the area so Mark would be able to finish high school with his friends. "They're fucking sell-outs."

He took the remote from where it had fallen on the floor, and attempted to turn the TV off, but Chelsea yanked it from his hands.

"Don't you *ever* try to turn off the TV in my house," she said, holding the remote close to Mark's head in a menacing pose. "Asshole."

Mark may have been my first real boyfriend, but Chelsea was my first real love.

***

Because of our instant prejudice towards Kurt and Courtney, it would be a little while before I would hear the music of Hole. Nirvana was much more accessible: they seemed to be everywhere, but I purposely didn't pay much attention. Learning that Kurt and Courtney were fans of one of my favorite writers, William S. Burroughs, and that Kurt had even gone to Kansas to hang out with him, did nothing to change my opinion. So what if both Kurt and Courtney were making music with Pat Smear of the Germs, one of our favorite bands? My friends and I had started doing heroin, and it was pretty obvious that Kurt and Courtney also did heroin, but we still told ourselves we could not relate. Was it just the times? Coincidence? Were we influenced by what was going on in Seattle, or was the scene playing out there just a microcosm of what it meant to be a young person at the time?

My mother forced me into rehab for the first time during my senior of high school. While I was there, Kurt left the rehab center he'd been forced into in California, went to the beautiful home he and Courtney had bought in Lake Washington, closed himself up in the greenhouse above the garage, and killed himself. I remember Chelsea, in tears, telling me this over the rehab payphone, and being shocked for a moment, then circling back to the attitude I espoused in all things Nirvana-related: cold, calculated dismissal. All of the empathy I'd feel for Kurt in life, and in death, would come later. My lack of empathy and my cold response to the news of his death would come to rate high on my list of regrets related to the precocious cynicism I felt when I was young. It seems like it should be an oxymoron: how can someone be so young, yet already so world-weary? In 1998, Courtney wrote a song called *Awful* for the Hole album *Celebrity Skin* that contains a lyric that when I think back to this time in my life I want to scream at myself:

Oh just shut up you're only sixteen

In the same payphone conversation with Chelsea, I remember changing the subject of Kurt's death to complain about the rehab staff taking away my Re/Search William S. Burroughs t-shirt. "Fucking assholes!" I said. "They're trying to rob me of my identity! They're trying to turn me into a *clone!*"

I want to smack myself.

***

A few days later, I was kicked out of rehab for refusing to leave my room. Subscribing to the same tough love philosophy that Courtney would later say she regretted using on Kurt during the final month of his life, my mother refused to let me come home, and I became homeless.

My friend Jeff worked at Record Town, and was a prisoner behind the counter as my friends and I came into the store and pillaged it of everything that even vaguely held our auditory interests. We were greedy and non-discriminating. I had Ozzy Osbourne box sets, Woodstock anniversary commemorative compilations, piles and piles of tapes and CDs that I never opened, and never planned on opening. They would come in handy later, when I started selling my possessions for money for drugs. Homeless, I tried to spend as much time as possible with my friends, but there were many hours I had no choice but to spend alone. One day I went to Record Town by myself, spent a few cursory minutes talking with Jeff, and then went over to the new music display to see what I could take. I spotted Hole's new album, *Live Through This*. The album seemed cursed, released only a week after Kurt's death, and with that eerily prescient title. It was for there for the taking. With none of my friends there to judge me, I slipped it into my bag.

Later that night, I went to a show in a far-off corner of Connecticut. The band was rather infamous in the area, and it was my first time seeing them play. I took an interest in their singer, Clem, a skinny, pale boy with a twitchy right eye. I thought his resemblance to Sid Vicious was uncanny. I approached him, and over the course of an awkward conversation, I mentioned to him that I was homeless.

"Where do you sleep?" Clem asked, sounding intrigued.

"I don't know," I answered. "Wherever."

"Where are you sleeping *tonight?*"

I told him that my friend and I had driven some distance for the show, and that after we returned, I'd probably sleep near her house, on the beach.

"I'll come with you," he offered.

In my friend's truck, Clem was being flirtatious, and starting rummaging through my bag, exposing the Hole tape. I immediately became defensive, expecting to hear the same dismissive comments about the band that I was so used to.

"I don't know why I took it," I began. "I don't even like them. I've never even heard them."

"You've never heard Hole?" Clem asked, either not noticing, or choosing not to call me out on the skewed logic of not liking a band that you've never heard. He handed the tape to my friend, who had a stereo in her truck. We listened to it on the drive back to town, where she dropped us off by the beach. I had heroin, and it turned out Clem was not at all comfortable with this. I'd completely misjudged him based on his appearance. Later that night, while I was nodding off, Clem attempted to run to the water and throw the drugs in, but I came to, and tackled him to the ground. Clearly, Clem and I were not going to work out. But on the car ride, he'd introduced me to a Hole song that I couldn't get out of my head. It was called *Rock Star*. Courtney had put it on *Live Through This* as an afterthought. *Rock Star* wasn't even the real name of the song, but the track listing for the album had already been printed; it was what the song would become known as:

When I went to school, in Olympia, and everyone's the same. We look the same, we talk the same, we even fuck the same

Before Clem would go his way, and me mine, he would tell me about going to see Nirvana play in 1991, at a club in New Haven called The Moon. "It was one of the best shows I've ever been to," he said. "It made me want to start a band."

***

Once Clem had opened my copy of *Live Through This*, I was exposed to the liner notes and the pictures inside.

Courtney in a tiara, short white dress, little girl tights and a fuzzy coat, smoking a cigarette.

When I'd left the rehab center after getting kicked out, I'd looked very much like this, minus the tiara. After seeing Courtney on television at Chelsea's house, I'd subtly adopted her look, though I would have denied that she'd been the inspiration, if anyone had asked. When I left Conifer Park Rehabilitation Center, marketed as *"a facility for the treatment of alcohol and drug dependency, located in the pines of Schenectady, New York,"* I was wearing a 60's style shift dress, ripped stockings, and my own fuzzy winter coat. I was almost three hours away from home. My mother had purposely sent me somewhere far away, thinking my friends would not travel the distance to pick me up should I try to leave. The rehab staff forced me to vacate the premises immediately. All I had with me was the clothing on my back, and the small antique first aid kit that I used as a purse. I later learned that the staff had called my mother—assuming that I would not be able to make it very far, they thought I would be forced to humble myself, and come back.

As I walked in the direction of what I hoped was downtown Schenectady, it began to snow. It was April, but it felt like mid-February, and I only had about two dollars' worth of change. I had no idea what I was going do. I thought my friend Amanda would probably come and get me, but I had no way to communicate with her. Even if I could get to a payphone, I would have to call her collect, and she was at school. For now, all I could do was walk. Eventually I came to a small supermarket. There was a bench outside, and I sat down. Cold, hungry, and feeling completely hopeless, I began to cry. People came in and out of the store, eyeing me suspiciously. Back home, I'd gotten used to being called a "freak" because of my appearance— I'd even fed off of it a little bit, me and what I told myself was my preternatural uniqueness. But on a cold bench, in a strange town, under falling snow, my uniqueness didn't carry any currency at all, it was all detriment. A little old man with a cane approached the store with an older woman. Instead of going inside with the woman, he whispered something to her, then sat down on the bench next to me. His companion hadn't tried to dissuade him, despite the cold, the snow, or me on the other end of the bench.

"What's the matter, young lady?" the man asked.

I had never felt so alone. I had gotten to the point in my crying where my body shook. What could I possibly say to this little old man that wouldn't make him grab his cane and hobble away from me?

"I'm far from home, and I can't get in touch with my friends," I stammered.

He seemed to think about this.

Feeling like I had nothing to lose, I took a chance, and told the man an amended version of the truth. I told him that I had left rehab, but changed the drug that had put me there from heroin to pot, thinking it would sound less severe. I made my mother out to be the villain of the story, portraying her as strict, unreasonable, and out of touch.

"Well," the old man said. "It's too cold for you to stay out here in what you have on. Let's go talk to my wife. I think she'll agree. We should take you back to our house until we can figure things out for you."

For all the things I didn't understand about the world, for all the things I dismissed, or viewed with a precocious sense of cynicism, I could see— even then— the gesture of this old man as a profound act of kindness; of caring. This little old man, who walked with a cane, so fragile and vulnerable, offering his home to this weird looking girl in overdone make-up and provocative clothing— this girl who had just told him that she'd left rehab.

As we walked the aisles of the supermarket looking for his wife, the man turned to me.

"You like loud music, don't you?" he said. "I bet you were a fan of that young man who just died in Seattle. It's so sad, you kids today. Killing yourselves as a form of expression."

I have to stop.

If I was an actor, and had to cry for a scene, all I would have to do is think of that little old man. He kills me every time.

***

In a 1995 *Spin* magazine interview, Courtney Love said, "I may lie a lot, but never in my lyrics."

It was the visual of Courtney Love that attracted me to her at first, then it was the sound of her band, Hole, (a sound that Billy Corgan once described as "someone screaming their head off, but in a very intelligent way") but what has kept me a fan of hers for the last twenty years is her lyrics. Her poetry. Some of the more famous lyrics from *Live Through This* have become so familiar, have been so oft-repeated, that to list them here almost feels redundant:

I don't really miss God, but I sure miss Santa Claus

I don't do the dishes. I throw them in the crib

I'm Miss World, somebody kill me

I want to be the girl with the most cake

Was she asking for it? Was she asking nice? If she was asking for it, did she ask you twice?

I've got a blister from touching everything I see

...but that's the fate of great poetry. Everybody owns it. It gets repeated ad infinitum, scrawled on backpacks, scribbled on the sides of buildings, recycled in ad campaigns, tattooed on body parts—why? Because it resonates. The lexicon of Courtney's lyrics is made up of girls (pee girl, retard girl, gutter girl, girl with the most cake), drugs, death, rebirth, boys, feminism, prostitution, California, dresses (both ripped, and on fire), Anne Boleyn, Hester Prynne, Yoko Ono, the internet, self-loathing, suicide, glamour, and children. It isn't surprising that Courtney chose to read from Sylvia Plath's *Daddy* in her tryout for a 1970's version of the *Mickey Mouse Club*. There's a lineage.

Courtney's lyrical composition is jarring. Despite Hole's embrace by mainstream audiences in the mid 1990's, Courtney's writing speaks of a very specific female perspective and experience. It's one that has never been represented in depth in mainstream music. The drugged and despairing, exploited yet optimistic, supersexual, whip-smart, body dysmorphic feminist. The voice in her lyrics is fucked beyond what we've been taught should ever be redeemable. The perspective is contradictory, and inconsistent. It is messy. It says, in spite of my ambition, I won't clean myself up. It says, literally, *don't you try to shut me up*; in spite of my mess, you will not dismiss me.

There are other lyrics of Courtney's, both pre and post *Live Through This*, that aren't as well known, but carry the same kind of weight, and power:

There is no power like my pretty power. There is no power like my ugly power

An eightball isn't love. A hooker's never gonna cum

They royalty rate all the girls like you. And they sell it out to the girls like you

Watch her wrap her legs around this world. You can't take the gutter from the girl

I don't believe in anything. I know that Mary lied

Does widespread, mainstream appeal detract from the emotional resonance of the sentiment conveyed?

I think of the closing line of one of the most famous poems in the world, Sylvia Plath's *Lady Lazarus*:

Out of the ash/I rise with my red hair/And I eat men like air.

The answer is *no*. What is it, then, that makes us back off once something passes through the pearly gates and gets embraced by mainstream society?

It's that desire to think of ourselves as unique, to rebel against that which is actually comforting: the idea of the universal experience. It has nothing to do with the validity of the music, or the poetry, or the sentiment conveyed. It's our want to think that we're the only one. That we are somehow... special. It's snobbery, and it's cynicism.

***

Whatever Courtney has experienced through the years, whatever she has *really* lived through, free from what we might think we know about her, free from any inside source exclusive reported on television or in the tabloids, I can see my life in her lyrics. We have had the same experiences. We have both lived our lives in the same almost constant state of contradiction. *Hooker waitress model actress oh just go nameless.* The lyrics of Courtney Love are my cultural zeitgeist. I read her lyrics— her poetry— and I can see the story of my life.

***

I have never met Courtney, nor do I want to. I've come close; with the advent of the internet, and her affection for the medium, I've talked with her a bit online. She gave me advice on how to get off Xanax once; another time, she messaged me to say that she was taking one of my Facebook statuses about how thunderstorms made me horny and texting it to a male friend. I don't want to meet Courtney, because really, in my mind anyway, she exists free of herself. She is a person of flesh and blood, but she is also an idea. When I finally stopped hiding the fact that she intrigued me, and started reading more about her and her life, I became fixated on something. Something probably totally insignificant to most people: that she was 25 when she started Hole. I fixated on this small detail because it gave me hope. I may have been 18, drug-addicted, and homeless, but knowing that Courtney was 25 when she started her band told me that I still had time. It wasn't over for me yet. You'll hear little kids talking about their role models, those people who give them something to aspire to beyond their circumstances. Courtney Love did that for me. When I was a fucked up kid, she gave me hope. Hope that I still had time. Time to take my mess, and make something out of it. Hopefully something beautiful.

Thank You

Jon Konrath, Marie Mundaca, Cynthia Santiglia, and Paul Corman-Roberts.

Kierstin Pupkowski and Corrine Seiser for all the years of reading.

Janet Steen for her generosity in helping to make "A Totally Gruesome Document" into something more cohesive.

Marc Bolan for *Laser Love*, yeah!, rock!, and *Thunderwing*. If the making of this book had a soundtrack, it would be almost entirely T-Rex, especially the albums *Electric Warrior*, *The Slider*, *Futuristic Dragon*, and *Dandy of the Underworld*.

And to Lisa, Lydia, Cookie, and Courtney.

When I first started working on this book, it contained poems, but as it progressed, the switch between formats didn't seem to me to benefit either. The title of the book comes from the last few lines of a poem of mine called *Blanche DuBois*.

> You should see me over here,
> drooling for ghosts.
> My inspiration is an old photograph of Richard Hell,
> just his face.
> I've known so many Richard Hells.
> There are more born every day that I want to touch.
> It pains me that beautiful boys get old.
> Hard in the face.

Jowled.
Nature is cruel with its weaponry of soft crowns and
paunches.
I want to love those boys.
I would accept no sass.
No flagrant show.
I would be satisfied
like Blanche DuBois, with a kiss.
My body would be
the kindest of strangers.

To M, G, N, and R, my gratitude and love.

About the Author

Fiona Helmsley is a writer of creative non-fiction, fiction, and poetry. Even before the internet, she always felt more comfortable sharing things with strangers over friends. This is her first book, though a claim could be made that it's her second. Her writing can be found online at sites like *The Weeklings* and *The Rumpus*, and in books like *The Best Sex Writing of the Year* and *Ladyland*. She loves her family. She misses people.

Also From Paragraph Line:

After the Jump
By John Sheppard

Frank Novak's seven-year-old daughter Audrey awakes one night screaming, "Get her out of me!" When he asks who, she replies, "Me!" It is the beginning of an adventure for the father and daughter that includes shadowy agents, alien invaders, two computer geniuses named "Steve," a homicidal child aviator, and Ronald Reagan.

Atmospheres
By Jon Konrath

No plot summary can suggest the mesmerizing texture of this caustically hilarious, aggressively mordant, constantly surprising and terrifyingly fun summation of the death-by-choking-on-hubris of the American dream in the 21st Century.

Kentucky Bestiary
By Joseph Hirsch

Welcome to Tipple Hollow, a rural Appalachian town where a mysterious and seemingly magical man has set up camp, claiming he has the power to rescue America from all of its worries. The only problem is that he may not be what he appears to be, and his dark secret may cost the people of Tipple Hollow their very souls.

Thunderbird
By Jon Konrath

A book whose skewed version of reality is more frighteningly and hilariously real than what is casually accepted by everyday readers as true-to-life. A complete wallop in the chops of conventional fiction by the author of the cult novel *Rumored to Exist*.

Keep in touch:

Visit paragraphline.com for all of our books, plus online fiction, the latest news on new releases, and more!

Made in the USA
San Bernardino, CA
12 March 2020